Hands-On
SCIENCE
ACTIVITIES

For Grades 3-4
Science Curriculum Activities Library
Book 2

Marvin N. Tolman

PARKER PUBLISHING COMPANY
West Nyack, New York 10994

Library of Congress Cataloging-in-Publication Data

Tolman, Marvin. N.
   Hands-on science activities for grades 3-4 / Marvin N. Tolman.
      p.   cm. — (Science curriculum activities library ; Book II)
   Includes bibliographic references.
   ISBN 0-13-011339-5
    1. Science teachers—Training of.   2. Science—Study and teaching
(Elementary)—Methodology.   3. Science—Study and teaching—Activity
programs. I. Title. II. Series: Science curriculum activities
library ; bk 2.
Q181.T59   1998
372.3'5044—dc21   98-29441
                                       CIP

© 1999 by
PARKER PUBLISHING COMPANY
West Nyack, New York

Printed in the United States of America

10 9 8 7 6 5 4 3 2 1

ISBN 0-13-011339-5

Computer illustrations by
Michelle Sullivan and
David Bentley

The activities in this resource were adapted from three specialized books in the "Science Problem-Solving Curriculum Library," including Hands-On Earth Science Activities for Grades K-8, Hands-On Life Science Activities for Grades K-8, Hands-On Physical Science Activities for Grades K-8, *all published in 1995 by Parker Publishing Company.*

PARKER PUBLISHING COMPANY
West Nyack, NY 10994

A Simon & Schuster Company

On the World Wide Web at http://www.phdirect.com

Prentice Hall International (UK) Limited, *London*
Prentice Hall of Australia Pty. Limited, *Sydney*
Prentice Hall Canada, Inc., *Toronto*
Prentice Hall Hispanoamericana, S.A., *Mexico*
Prentice Hall of India Private Limited, *New Delhi*
Prentice Hall of Japan, Inc., *Tokyo*
Simon & Schuster Asia Pte. Ltd., *Singapore*
Editora Prentice Hall do Brasil, Ltda., *Rio de Janerio*

ABOUT THE
SCIENCE CURRICULUM ACTIVITIES LIBRARY

The *Science Curriculum Activities Library* provides teachers with nearly 500 activities that give students hands-on experience related to earth, life, and physical science topics covered in the K-6 curriculum. The activities follow the discovery/inquiry approach and encourage students to analyze, synthesize, and infer based on their own hands-on exploration.

For easy use, the activities are organized into three separately printed grade-level books, each containing a selection of age-appropriate investigations in the different fields of science. The books are individually titled:

- *Hands-on Science Activities for Grades K-2*
- *Hands-on Science Activities for Grades 3-4*
- *Hands-on Science Activities for Grades 5-6*

All of the activities in each grade-level volume are tested, complete, and ready for use with virtually any science program or text and with students of varying ability levels.

More than ever before, children of today grow up in a world impacted by science and technology. A basic understanding of nature and an appreciation for the world around them are gifts too valuable to deny these precious young people who will be the problem solvers of tomorrow. In addition, a strong science program with a discovery/inquiry approach can enrich the development of mathematics, reading, social studies, and other areas of the curriculum. The activities in the *Library* develop these skills. Most activities call for thoughtful responses, with questions that encourage analyzing, synthesizing, and inferring instead of simply answering yes or no.

Development of thinking and reasoning skills, in addition to learning basic content information, are the main goals of these hands-on activities. Learning how to learn and how to apply the various tools of learning are more useful in a person's life than is the acquisition of large numbers of scientific facts. Students are encouraged to explore, invent, and create as they develop skills with the processes of science. The learning of scientific facts is a byproduct of this effort, and increased insight and retention associated with facts learned are virtually assured.

ABOUT THE AUTHOR

Dr. Marvin N. Tolman

Trained as an educator at Utah State University and the University of Utah, Marv Tolman began his career as a teaching principal in rural southeastern Utah. The next eleven years were spent teaching grades one through six in schools of San Juan and Utah Counties, and earning graduate degrees.

Currently professor of elementary education, Dr. Tolman has been teaching graduate and undergraduate courses at Brigham Young University since 1975. Subject areas of his courses include math methods, science methods, and formerly computer literacy for teachers. He has served as a consultant to school districts, taught workshops in many parts of the United States, and published numerous articles in professional journals. Dr. Tolman is one of two authors of *What Research Says to the Teacher: The Computer and Education* (co-author Dr. Ruel Allred), published in 1984 by the National Education Association, and a co-author of *Computers in Education*, published by Allyn & Bacon, 1996 (3rd edition). Dr. Tolman also wrote *Discovering Elementary Science: Method, Content, and Problem-Solving Activities*, 2nd ed., (co-author Dr. Garry R. Hardy), 1999, Allyn & Bacon. With Dr. James O. Morton, Dr. Tolman wrote the three-book series of elementary science activities called the *Science Curriculum Activities Library*, 1986, Parker Publishing Co.

Dr. Tolman now lives with his wife, Judy, in Spanish Fork, Utah, where they have raised five children.

ACKNOWLEDGMENTS

Mentioning the names of all individuals who contributed to the *Science Curriculum Activities Library* would require an additional volume. The author is greatly indebted to the following:

- Teachers and students of all levels.

- School districts throughout the United States who cooperated by supporting and evaluating ideas and methods used in this book.

- Dr. James O. Morton, my mentor and my dear friend.

- Dr. Garry R. Hardy, my teaching partner for the past many years, for his constant encouragement and creative ideas.

- Finally, my angel Judy, for without her love, support, encouragement, patience, and acceptance, these books could never have been completed.

HOW TO USE THIS BOOK

This book consists of 193 easy-to-use, hands-on activities in the following 20 areas of earth, life, and physical sciences:

Earth Science	Life Science	Physical Science
• Water	• Plants and Seeds	• Nature of Matter
• Weather	• Animals	• Energy
• The Earth	• Growing and Changing: Animal Life Cycles	• Light
• Ecology		• Sound
• Above the Earth	• Animal Adaptations	• Simple Machines
• Beyond the Earth	• Body Systems	• Magnetism
	• The Five Senses	• Static Electricity
	• Health and Nutrition	

Teacher Qualifications

Two important qualities of the elementary teacher as a scientist are (1) commitment to helping students acquire learning skills and (2) recognition of the value of science and its implications in the life and learning of the child.

You do not need to be a scientist to conduct an effective and exciting science program at the elementary level. Interest, creativity, enthusiasm, and willingness to get involved and try something new are the qualifications the teacher of elementary science needs most. If you haven't really tried teaching hands-on science, you will find it to be a lot like eating peanuts—you can't eat just one. Try it. The excitement and enthusiasm you see in your students will bring you back to it again and again.

Capitalize on Interest

These materials are both nongraded and nonsequential. Areas of greatest interest and need can be emphasized. As you gain experience with using the activities, your skill in guiding students toward appropriate discoveries and insights will increase.

Organizing for an Activity-centered Approach

Current trends encourage teachers to use an activity-based program, supplemented by the use of textbooks and many other reference materials. The activities herein encourage hands-on discovery, which enhances the development of valuable learning skills through direct experience.

One of the advantages of this approach is the elimination of the need for all students to have the same book at the same time, freeing a substantial portion of the textbook money for purchasing a variety of materials and references, including other textbooks, trade books, audio and video tapes, videodiscs, models, and other visuals. References should be acquired that lend themselves developmentally to a variety of approaches, subject matter emphases, and levels of reading difficulty.

Grabbers

The sequence of activities within the sections of this book is flexible, and may be adjusted according to interest, availability of materials, time of year, or other factors. Most of the activities in each section can be used independently as *grabbers*, to capture student interest. Used this way, they can help to achieve several specific objectives:

- To assist in identifying student interests and selecting topics for study.

- To provide a wide variety of interesting and exciting hands-on activities from many areas of science. As students investigate activities that are of particular interest, they will likely be motivated to try additional related activities in the same section of the book.

- To introduce teachers and students to the discovery/inquiry approach.

- To be used for those occasions when only a short period of time is available and a high-interest independent activity is needed.

Unique Features

The following points should be kept in mind while using this book:

1. Most of these activities can be used with several grade levels, with little adaptation.

2. The student is the central figure when using the discovery/inquiry approach to hands-on learning.

3. The main goals are problem solving and the development of critical-thinking skills. The learning of content is a spin-off, but it is possibly learned with greater insight and meaning than if it were the main objective.

4. It attempts to prepare teachers for inquiry-based instruction and to sharpen their guidance and questioning techniques.

5. Most materials needed for the activities are readily available in the school or at home.

6. Activities are intended to be open and flexible and to encourage the extension of skills through the use of as many outside resources as possible: (a) The use of parents, aides, and resource people of all kinds is recommended throughout; (b) the library, media center, and other school resources, as well as classroom reading centers related to the areas of study, are essential in the effective teaching and learning of science; and (c) educational television and videos can greatly enrich the science program.

7. With the exception of the activities labeled "teacher demonstration" or "whole-class activity," students are encouraged to work individually, in pairs, or in small groups. In most cases the teacher gathers and organizes the materials, arranges the learning setting, and serves as a resource person. In many instances, the materials listed and the procedural steps are all students will need in order to perform the activities.

8. Information is given in "To the Teacher" at the beginning of each section and in "Teacher Information" at the end of each activity to help you develop your content background and your questioning and guidance skills, in cases where such help is needed. For teachers who desire additional background information on elementary science topics, the following book written by the same author is recommended: *Discovering Elementary Science: Method, Content, and Problem-Solving Activities*, 2nd ed. (co-author Dr. Garry R. Hardy), 1999, Allyn & Bacon.

9. Full-page activity sheets are offered when needed throughout the book. These sheets can easily be reproduced and kept on hand for student use.

At the end of the book are a bibliography, sources of free and inexpensive materials, and a list of science supply houses, as well as sources for video tapes, videodiscs, and computer software. This information can save you time in locating additional resources and materials.

Final Note

Discovering the excitement of science and developing new techniques for critical thinking and problem solving should be the major goals of elementary science. The discovery/inquiry approach also must emphasize verbal responses and discussion. *It is important that students experience many hands-on activities* in their learning of science *and that they talk about what they do*. Each child should have many opportunities to describe observations and to explain what they do and why. With the exception of recording observations, these activities usually do not require extensive writing, but that, too, is a skill that can be enriched through interest and involvement in science.

There is an ancient Chinese saying: "A journey of a thousand miles begins with a single step." May the ideas and activities in this book help to provide that first step.

Marvin N. Tolman

CONTENTS

Section One
EARTH SCIENCE ACTIVITIES 1

Topic 1   Water • 3

Topic 2 WEATHER · 11

Topic 3 The Earth · 23

Topic 4 Ecology · 41

Topic 5   Above the Earth • 79

Topic 6   Beyond the Earth • 103

Section Two
LIFE SCIENCE ACTIVITIES   129

Topic 7   Plants and Seeds • 131

Topic 8   Animals • 153

Topic 13   Health and Nutrition • 245

Section Three
PHYSICAL SCIENCE ACTIVITIES   255

Topic 14   Nature of Matter • 257

Topic 18   Simple Machines • 341

Topic 19   Magnetism • 357

Topic 20   Static Electricity • 363

LISTING OF ACTIVITIES BY TOPIC AND SUBTOPIC

WATER

Subtopic	Activities	
Buoyancy	1.6	
Effect of Heat on Water	1.5	
Effect of Salt Water	1.4	
Effect of Water on Light	1.2	1.3
Water Pressure	1.1	

WEATHER

Subtopic	Activities		
Precipitation	2.1	2.4	
Measuring the Atmosphere			
Wind Speed	2.2	2.3	
Predicting	2.5	2.6	2.7

BEYOND THE EARTH

Subtopic	Activities				
Earth as a Planet	6.1				
Earth Movements	6.2	6.3	6.4		
Moon	6.6	6.7	6.8	6.9	
Satellites	6.5	6.6			
Solar System	6.10	6.11	6.12	6.13	6.14

PLANTS AND SEEDS

Subtopic	Activities			
Growing Plants	7.1	7.2		
Mold (not a plant)	7.9	7.10	7.11	7.12
Plant Parts	7.3	7.4	7.5	7.6
Plants for Food	7.7	7.8		

ANIMALS

Subtopic	Activities			
Animal Characteristics	8.1			
Aquarium	8.7			
Bird Homes	8.6			
Nature Squares	8.2	8.3	8.4	8.5
Terrarium	8.8			
Tiny Living Creatures (not animals)		8.9		

GROWING AND CHANGING: ANIMAL LIFE CYCLES

Subtopic	Activities	
Butterflies	9.1	
Length of Life	9.3	
Mealworms	9.2	

ANIMAL ADAPTATIONS

Subtopic	Activities	
Communication	10.3	
Design a Bird	10.6	
Movements	10.2	
Seasonal Adaptations	10.4	10.5
What Is Adaptation?	10.1	

BODY SYSTEMS

Subtopic	Activities		
Blood Pressure and Pulse	11.1	11.2	
Bones	11.7	11.8	11.9
Lungs	11.4		
Muscles	11.10	11.11	
Nails	11.12		
Skin	11.5	11.6	
Systems	11.3		

THE FIVE SENSES

Subtopic	Activities					
Hearing	12.7	12.8	12.9	12.10		
Sight	12.1	12.2	12.3			
Smell	12.4	12.5	12.6			
Taste	12.12	12.13	12.14			
Touch	12.2	12.15	12.16	12.17	12.18	12.19

HEALTH AND NUTRITION

Subtopic	Activities	
Body Makeup	13.1	
Common and Popular Foods	13.3	
Food Groups	13.2	13.3

NATURE OF MATTER

Subtopic	Activities	
Elements, Compounds	14.5	
Mixtures and Solutions	14.2	14.3
Physical and Chemical Changes	14.4	
Surface Tension	14.1	

ENERGY

LIGHT

SOUND

MACHINES

MAGNETISM

STATIC ELECTRICITY

EARTH SCIENCE ACTIVITIES

Topics

- **Water**
- **Weather**
- **The Earth**
- **Ecology**
- **Above the Earth**
- **Beyond the Earth**

Topic 1:   Water

TO THE TEACHER

Water is essential to all forms of life. People can live for weeks without food but only for a short period of time without water. Because it is usually available we often take it for granted, yet it plays an important role in almost every area of science. Even the study of nonliving materials includes the study of how water acts upon and interacts with them.

Water is the most abundant substance on the planet, yet much of the earth suffers from water shortages. Huge amounts of water are required for agriculture, for the manufacture of goods, for personal needs, and for many other purposes. Although there is a global abundance of water, getting the right amounts in the right places and in the right form is a constant challenge in many parts of the world.

Water evaporates into the air, then condenses and returns to the surface of the earth in various forms of precipitation. Called the *water cycle*, this process is vital to all forms of life as it recycles and redistributes this precious resource.

Activity 1.1
HOW CAN WE SEE WATER PRESSURE?

Materials Needed

- Gallon can or plastic bottle
- Nail
- Hammer

Procedure

1. Use the nail to punch three holes, equally spaced from top to bottom, in the can or plastic bottle.
2. Place the container in the sink and hold all three holes while filling it with water.
3. Release all three holes at the same time.
4. What happened? What does this tell you about the weight and pressure of water?

For Problem Solvers: Repeat this activity using containers of different diameters and different height. Place all containers the same distance from the ground. Let your measure of water pressure be the distance of the stream from the container when it reaches the ground. What variable seems to make the difference? Diameter of the container? Height of the container? Depth of the water? All of these? What seems to make the difference?

Do some research on depth of water in dams and oceans, and on the pressure of water at the bottom. When water comes through the bottom of a dam and runs through a turbine to spin a generator, what is the pressure of the water at that point? Is it the same for all dams?

What is the water pressure at the deepest part of the ocean? Could you survive there without protection? How do fish live deep in the sea? Could all fish live miles below the surface? What would happen if they came quickly to the surface?

Teacher Information

The stream of water will be greatest from the lowest hole. Less will flow from the middle hole and least from the top hole.

This demonstrates that the pressure of water increases with its depth. (This is also true of air pressure. Pressure at sea level is much greater than at 10,000 feet.)

Your problem solvers will learn that water pressure is directly affected by depth of the water. Pressure of water coming through the bottom of a dam is the same at a given depth whether there is a half mile of water backed up behind the dam or 40 miles of water backed up behind the dam.

INTEGRATING: Math, reading, social studies

SKILLS: Observing, inferring, measuring, predicting, communicating, comparing and contrasting, formulating hypotheses, identifying and controlling variables, experimenting, researching

Activity 1.2
HOW CAN YOU POUR LIGHT?

(Enrichment activity)

Materials Needed

- Tall, slim jar (olive jar)
- Flashlight
- Hammer
- Nail
- Newspaper or light cardboard
- Masking tape or plastic tape
- Water

Procedure

1. With the hammer and nail, make two holes in the lid of the jar. The holes should be near the edge but opposite each other. One hole should be quite small. Work the nail around in the other to enlarge the hole a bit.
2. Fill the jar about two thirds full of water and put the lid on.
3. Put tape over the holes in the lid until you are ready to pour.
4. Lay the jar and flashlight end to end, with the face of the flashlight at the bottom of the jar.
5. Roll the newspaper or cardboard around the jar and flashlight to enclose them in a light-tight tube. Tape the tube together so it will stay.
6. Slide the flashlight out of the tube, turn it on, and slide it back into the tube.
7. Hold the apparatus upright and remove the tape from the lid. With the large nail hole down, pour the water into the pan.
8. What happened to the beam of light as the water poured into the pan?
9. Do you have any idea what causes this?

For Problem Solvers: Use your creativity with this activity. Try different containers for the water, and different light sources. Try putting some food coloring in the water. Does that provide the same effect as if you put a colored filter over the flashlight?

Teacher Information

Although light travels in straight lines, it is reflected internally at the water's surface and follows the path of the stream of water. Because of the phenomenon of internal reflection, fiber optics can be used to direct light anywhere a wire can go, even into the veins and arteries of the human body.

Refraction occurs as light changes speed in passing from one medium to another.

Reflection commonly refers to the bouncing of light in a single medium, in this case water or plastic.

SKILLS: Observing, inferring, communicating, formulating hypotheses, experimenting

Activity 1.3
WHAT DO BEARS KNOW THAT MANY PEOPLE DON'T?

Materials Needed

- 8-ounce water glass
- Pencil
- Water

Procedure

1. Use an 8-ounce glass about two thirds full of water.
2. Put a pencil in the glass. Observe the pencil above and below the water level.
3. What can you say about this?
4. Why do you think this might be called "What do bears know that people don't?" Think of a bear trying to catch a fish it sees in the water.

For Problem Solvers: Challenge your friends to a test of skills at spear fishing. Put some water in a dishpan or sink. Place a coin (that's the fish) at the bottom of the pan. Use a meter stick, a metal rod, or any other straight and narrow shaft as a spear. Place the tip of your spear on the edge of the pan, but not in the water. Aim at the fish, and quickly push the spear to the bottom of the pan, being sure to keep the spear at the same angle as when it was aimed.

Talk about eagles and bears, and their ability to strike at the right place when catching a fish. How do you think they learned to do that?

Teacher Information

When the pencil is put in the glass of water, it appears to bend as it enters the water. This is because the light is bent as it enters the water. Actually, the pencil is not where it appears to be under the water. Bears seem to know this and use it when fishing. They know where the fish is even though it isn't exactly where it appears to be.

Children may also notice that the pencil appears larger under the water. This is because the curved surface of the glass and the water in it act as a convex lens.

INTEGRATING: Language arts

SKILLS: Observing, inferring, estimating, communicating

Activity 1.4
WHAT CAN YOU LEARN FROM AN EGG?

 Take home and do with family and friends.

Materials Needed

- Egg
- Glass full of water
- Salt

Procedure

1. Put the egg in a glass of water.
2. Add salt a tablespoon at a time, and stir until something happens to the egg. What happened?
3. Can you explain what happened?

Teacher Information

When the egg is put in the untreated water, it will sink to the bottom of the glass. As salt is added to the water, the egg will rise and float on top. This is because salt increases the density of the water until the egg is able to float.

Floating an egg in brine solution is the method some people use to tell when the brine is just right for pickling.

SKILLS: Observing, inferring, comparing and contrasting

8

Activity 1.5
HOW DOES TEMPERATURE AFFECT THE SPEED OF MOLECULES?

Materials Needed

- Two clear glasses
- Food coloring
- Paper and pencil
- Two eye droppers
- Hot water
- Cold water

Procedure

1. Put very cold water in one tumbler and hot water in the other. Fill each about half full.
2. Draw four or five drops of food coloring into each of the two eye droppers. Put as near the same amount in each as possible.
3. Hold a dropper over each tumbler and squeeze to empty the contents of both at exactly the same time.
4. Compare the movement of the color in the two containers. In which tumbler did the color spread more rapidly?
5. If you have time, try different colors and different water temperatures. Record your observations.

For Problem Solvers: Now measure the temperatures of your hot and cold water and measure the time required for the food coloring to completely disperse through the water. Put water in a third container, being sure that the temperature is different from either of the first two by several degrees. Predict the time required for the color to spread throughout the water in the third container. Test your prediction.

Do all of the colors spread through the water at the same speed? What is your hypothesis? Design a test to find out, then try it. Was your hypothesis correct?

Teacher Information

As temperatures increase, molecules move faster. The food coloring will diffuse noticeably more rapidly in the hot water than in the cold water. In this activity, water temperature is the variable. You might have students try the same activity with color as the variable. For instance, use two tumblers of cold water and put red in one and green (or blue) in the other.

You might also consider having students use a stopwatch and a thermometer and record the actual time required for maximum diffusion (equal color throughout, as judged by the student).

Try it with different measured temperatures and graph the results. Have students use early results from the graph to predict diffusion time for each new temperature.

SKILLS: Observing, inferring, measuring, predicting, communicating, comparing and contrasting, using space-time relationships, formulating hypotheses, identifying and controlling variables, experimenting

Activity 1.6
HOW DO RAISINS SWIM?

 Take home and do with family and friends.

Materials Needed

- Clear carbonated soda
- Pint-sized fruit jar
- Several raisins

Procedure

1. Add clear carbonated soda to the jar until it is about two thirds full.
2. Put several raisins into the jar with the soda. Observe for several minutes. What happened? What can you say about this?

Teacher Information

When the raisins are put into the soda, they will sink to the bottom of the jar. Gradually, small bubbles of carbon dioxide gas from the soda will collect on the skins of the raisins. Enough bubbles of gas will soon have collected on the surface of the raisins to make them buoyant and they will float to the surface of the soda. As soon as the raisins reach the surface, the bubbles pop and the raisins sink to the bottom. This action will continue for some time.

SKILLS: Observing, inferring

Topic 2:   Weather

TO THE TEACHER

Weather is crucial in our lives. It influences where we live, what (and if) we eat, what we wear, what we do, and, sometimes, how we feel. Weather appears as a part of the first recorded history of man. Early civilizations grew and developed in favorable climates. The history of man is interwoven with myths, legends, stories, customs, religious beliefs, poems, art, music, dancing, and many other expressions that tell the story of man's continuing concern with the mysteries, beauties, and dangers of the often unpredictable nature of weather.

Today, sophisticated weather instruments circle the earth to report weather conditions on a global scale. Countless weather stations, with both professional and amateur meteorologists, study and report on a daily basis, yet frequently the news carries a report of some unpredicted or unusual occurrence. This section should help students understand some of the many variables that must be taken into account in a study of weather and to appreciate its importance in our lives.

Several activities require simple construction. Please take time to read all the activities before you begin. Parents and other resource people can be a great help in gathering and assisting as you build a weather station and a convection box. Be sure to plan to construct several of each of them.

Using the weather station and other sources to predict weather should take two to four weeks. However, it should not require too much time each day, so another section could be undertaken at the same time.

We hope you will use poetry, stories, music, and art liberally throughout the study.

Finally, please don't blame the weather on the weather forecaster.

Activity 2.1
HOW CAN YOU MAKE RAIN?

(Teacher-supervised activity)

Materials Needed

- Quart-sized glass jar
- Aluminum or iron pie tin
- Hot water
- Ice cubes

Procedure

1. Pour a cup of hot water in a quart-sized glass jar. (No lid is needed.)
2. Put some ice cubes in a pie tin and place it on top of the jar.
3. Observe for several minutes. What happened?

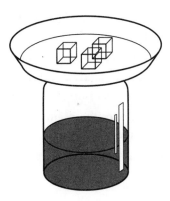

Jar with Water in Bottom and Ice Cubes on Top

Teacher Information

The hot water will heat the air in the jar and add moisture to it. The moisture-laden hot air will rise. As it nears the cold pie tin, the air will cool and condense. In time, it may actually begin to "rain" outside the jar, as water drops form on, and fall from, the part of the pan overhanging the jar.

Activity 2.2
HOW CAN WIND SPEED BE MEASURED?

(Teacher-supervised activity)

Materials Needed

- Support base
- Two strips of lath 40 cm (16 in.) long
- Four paper cups (3 of one color and 1 of a different color)
- Thumbtacks
- Glass eye dropper or very thin glass bottle
- Strong glue
- Small 2 cm (3/4 in.) nails
- Hammer
- Drill

Procedure

1. Find the middle of each lath, cross one on top of the other, and glue them together. Use two small nails to hold them securely.

2. Have your teacher drill a hole in the exact center of the cross, large enough to accommodate the eye dropper or bottle.

3. Use or build a support base. (See Nail, Support, Base below.)

4. Glue a 4-ounce paper cup to each of the four ends of the cross. Use thumbtacks, too, for extra strength. Be sure the open ends of all the cups face in the same direction.

5. Put the eye dropper in the cross over the point on the support base. When completed, the cross and cups should spin freely.

6. This instrument is called an anemometer (see figure below), and it is used to measure wind speed.

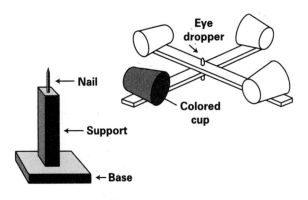

Homemade Anemometer

For Problem Solvers: Wind speed can be measured with instruments of different types. Can you think of another way to make an instrument that could indicate wind speed? It doesn't need to be like the one above. See what you can learn about other types of anemometers. Build one or more of them. Design your own anemometer.

Do some research and find out how meteorologists measure wind speed. Is there any resemblance between their instrument and yours?

Teacher Information

It is very important that the anemometer be balanced and spin freely. A parent or aide could be enlisted to use a hand drill to bore the holes in the cross pieces.

The next activity will help students use the anemometer to measure wind speed fairly accurately.

INTEGRATING: Reading, social studies, art

SKILLS: Observing, comparing and contrasting, measuring, identifying and controlling variables, experimenting, researching

Activity 2.3
HOW DOES AN ANEMOMETER WORK?

(Do this in moderate wind)

Materials Needed

- Anemometer constructed in Activity 2.2
- Stopwatch or watch with second hand
- Paper
- Pencil
- Masking tape

Procedure

1. Take the materials to an open area where a mild wind is blowing.
2. Put the anemometer on a flat surface where it will spin freely. Put a strip of masking tape on the flat surface under the cups so they will pass over it each time they spin around.
3. Use the colored cup as a counter and mark each time it passes over the strip during a 60-second period.
4. Divide the number of times the colored cup passes over the strip by 10 and you will have the approximate speed of the wind.
5. Repeat steps 1–4 each day at the same time the wind direction is checked with the wind vane. Keep a record of the date, time, and wind speed for 30 days.

For Problem Solvers: Here's another way you can calibrate your anemometer. On a calm, windless day, get someone to drive you to a back road that has very little traffic. Hold your anemometer out the window while the driver holds the speed at exactly five miles per hour. Count and record the revolutions of the anemometer in one minute. Do the same at 10 mph and at 15 mph, etc., and your anemometer is calibrated. Don't go too fast, or your anemometer will blow away.

Teacher Information

Friction will be an important factor in the accuracy of the anemometer. You can calibrate the accuracy to some degree if on a very calm day you hold the anemometer out the window of a car at various speeds while counting the number of spins. If the car is driven for one minute at 5, 10, and 15 miles per hour, you should have enough data to compare with the stationary recordings. The anemometer must be held far enough away from the car so air currents caused by the car do not disturb it.

SKILLS: Observing, measuring, using space-time relationships

Activity 2.4
HOW CAN RAINFALL BE MEASURED?

(Rain is needed for this activity)

Materials Needed

- Straight-sided water glass or can at least 20 cm (8 in.) tall
- Ruler or meter stick
- Paper
- Pencil

Procedure

1. When rain is expected, take the can or glass outside to a place where there are no buildings, walls, trees, or other obstructions nearby.

2. As soon as possible after the rain stops, use the ruler to measure the amount of water in the container.

3. Rainfall is usually reported in inches or centimeters.

4. Keep a chart for 30 days, listing the date and the amount of rain.

5. If you are studying weather at a time when most of the precipitation is snow, you can measure snow depth with the meter stick if you are in an open area.

6. If you are measuring precipitation in the form of snow, sleet, or hail, you can collect it in a wastebasket or pail, bring it into a warm place to melt and measure the water content. Different types of snow contain varying amounts of water for a given volume.

For Problem Solvers: How many centimeters or inches of precipitation does your area get in a year, on the average? What times of the year does most of the precipitation come? Does most of it come in the form of rain, or is it mostly from snowfall? Find a rainfall map and compare your area with other parts of the nation and of the world.

Teacher Information

Some rain gauges use a funnel at the top of the collector. This is helpful in collecting rain, but you should take into account the diameter of the funnel versus the diameter of the container and correct your measurement accordingly. Divide the area of the funnel opening by the area of a cross section of the container. Moisture content is very important in measuring snow. Five cm (2 in.) of wet snow may contain more moisture than 20 cm (8 in.) of powdery snow. If a slight amount of rain falls, but is not measurable, it should be recorded as a "trace."

INTEGRATING: Math, reading, social studies

SKILLS: Communicating, using space-time relationships, researching

Activity 2.5
HOW CAN YOU OPERATE A WEATHER STATION?

(Class-planning activity)

Materials Needed

- Large sheet of paper for sample "Weather Chart" (See page 19.)
- Meter stick
- Crayons
- Markers

Procedure

1. Now that you have instruments to record the weather, plan a 30-day chart to record it.

    Use the sample "Weather Chart" as a starting point.

    You will need to decide the data you want to record each day and assign committees to record it.

2. The Weather Bureau uses standard symbols to indicate weather conditions. Your teacher can help you find a book to help you learn to use these symbols if you care to.

3. Leave four extra columns at the end to record weather reports from other sources and to record the actual weather.

4. In addition to the large bulletin board chart, you may want to make smaller copies for your own use.

For Problem Solvers: With this activity, try your hand at predicting the weather. Make another column at the right end of the chart and label it "Tomorrow's Forecast." In this column write your forecast for each day, one day in advance. Pay particular attention to the barometric pressure each day. Notice the kind of changes in the weather that follow a rise in pressure, and the kinds of changes that follow a drop in pressure. This information will help you make your daily forecasts.

Teacher Information

The official Weather Bureau symbols are much more complicated and usually unnecessary to use for a short period of time. The chart in the example provides for 15 days. This is a minimum recommended time for the study. Thirty days would provide for a more accurate comparison. Daily readings should take only a few minutes, so other science projects could be planned for the remaining time.

SKILLS: Observing, inferring, classifying, measuring, predicting, communicating, using space-time relationships, formulating hypotheses, identifying variables

Key ✱

Symbol	Condition
○	Clear Sky
◑	Partly Cloudy
●	Rain
✳	Snow
⬈	Thunder Storm
◗	Drizzle
‖‖	Fog
⬴	Warm Front
⬴⬴	Cold Front
⬍	Dust Storm
▷	Showers
◈	Hail
◁	Sleet
◇	Smoke
8	Haze

✱ (not an official key)

●● more symbols-stronger conditions

✱▷ symbol above symbol-mixed conditions

Date	Time	Temp	Wind Speed	Wind Direction	Humidity	Air Pressure	Tomorrow's Forecast				Today's Actual Weather
							Class	Commercial	Weather Bureau TV, Radio, News	Farmers Almanac	

Sample Weather Chart

19

Activity 2.6
WHAT IS THE BEST SOURCE OF INFORMATION FOR PREDICTING WEATHER?

(Group activity)

Materials Needed

- Weather instruments constructed in previous activities
- Commercial weather instruments manufactured for home use
- *The Old Farmers Almanac*
- Pencil
- A single professional source for weather reporting, such as a newspaper, television, radio, or the United States Weather Bureau
- Weather chart from Activity 2.5

Procedure

1. Your teacher will tell you about four different methods you can use to predict weather. Choose one of the four and form a "weather team."

2. For the next several weeks, meet with your group, study the information you have collected from your source for the day, and record your group's prediction of what tomorrow's weather will be on the chart.

3. At the end of the week, compare each of the predictions with actual weather as it occurred. If your predictions were not accurate, try to think of ways to improve them.

Teacher Information

The main objective of this activity is to help students become aware of some of the major factors that are considered in weather forecasting.

Commercial weather instruments for home use are sold in many stores. They usually consist of a thermometer, aneroid barometer, and hygrometer. You can probably borrow a set from someone in your school or community.

In selecting a professional source, try to locate an individual with whom you can work. This person can become an excellent resource and may be able to assist by providing materials and arranging field trips. If you make daily contact with an agency by telephone, be certain only one student is selected to make the call.

Long-term predictions are not included in this activity. However, this would be an appropriate time to introduce the use of current technology such as weather satellites, Doppler radar, international observatories, and cloud-seeding techniques to predict and influence the weather (see encyclopedia and books on weather from your library).

INTEGRATING: Reading, language arts, social studies

SKILLS: Observing, communicating, using space-time relationships, formulating hypotheses, identifying variables, researching

Activity 2.7
WHAT ARE SOME UNUSUAL WAYS TO PREDICT AND EXPLAIN WEATHER?

(A just-for-fun activity)

Materials Needed

- Books and stories
- Traditions and myths
- Older adults

Procedure

1. Groundhog Day is known and observed almost everywhere in the United States. Find out all you can about this special day and share with your class.

2. Below are listed a number of other ways people use to predict weather. How many do you know? Can you complete the sentences?

    Woolly caterpillars tell us _____

    Amount of fur or fat on animals tells us _____

    The Indians say _____

    My grandmother's arthritis _____

    My grandfather's corns _____

    The animals (squirrels, birds, etc.) are _____

    A ring around the moon means _____

    Red sky at night, sailors delight; red sky at morning, sailors take _____

    A "rain dance" is _____

    When north winds blow, _____

3. Form a committee and find out as much as you can about folk methods for predicting and changing weather.

4. With your teacher's help, make an illustrated book on folk weather.

Teacher Information

Although it is not scientific, this activity may help children become aware of the many ways people have used to understand, predict, and influence the weather. Weather conditions in some manner influence many factors in our lives and, in fact, indirectly or directly determine our existence. Technology has enabled us to walk on the moon, circle the earth in an hour, see an event as it happens anywhere on earth—yet we are all at the mercy of the weather, just as we were centuries ago.

In your book of folk weather, be sure to include songs, poems, stories, and pictures to portray the feelings of mystery, power, beauty, wonder, and awe of that remarkable phenomenon we call weather.

Finally, remember the old saying, "It always rains on the weathermen's picnic."

INTEGRATING: Reading, language arts, social studies

SKILLS: Communicating, researching

Topic 3:   The Earth

TO THE TEACHER

We live on a combination of rock, soil, and water known as the earth's crust. We depend on this relatively thin layer (along with air and sunlight) to provide our food, medicine, and clothing—and the materials to build our homes, cars, and other things. Geologists continually search the earth's surface for clues to the location of mineral resources and answers to questions about the origin, early history, and current changes of the surface of this planet. A study of its structure and evolutionary history helps to increase our appreciation for the earth and its resources.

Scientists are interested in the composition of the earth, the forces that shape and change it, and how it came to be as it is. From a career point of view, exposure to some of these ideas can help students begin to develop a perception of geology-related occupations and even stimulate possible early interests. From the standpoint of general interest, horizons are broadened within the mind as students acquire a glimpse of the significance and majesty of this great planet.

The first several activities of this unit are map oriented. The objective of these activities is not to present a thorough treatment of map reading, but to develop the concept of representing the earth, or small portions of it, on paper or other surface that can be used for observation and study. The map-related questions in this section deal with the problems arising from efforts to represent size and shape in miniature form. Even in the very early grades, students can begin forming concepts about the earth's magnitude and structure.

Children are natural collectors. This interest can be stimulated and broadened by encouraging them to watch for new kinds of rocks; then provide simple ideas for recognizing likenesses and differences in rocks they find and categorizing them according to those recognized attributes.

Along with involvement in the activities of this section, emphasis should be placed on appropriate geologic concepts. The earth's crust, for instance, consists largely of rock layers that have been formed and layered by such factors as heat, pressure, and the effects of water and cementing material. Under the earth's crust is molten rock, called magma. Great pressures sometimes force magma to the surface, forming volcanoes. Other forces shift the outer layers of the earth's surface, causing earthquakes and forming mountains and valleys, sometimes causing much destruction in life and property.

Many locations are rich with nearby sites where geologic changes are evident—exposed rock layers on a mountainside or at an excavation site, a glacier-formed canyon, or a terrace that was once the beach of an ancient lake. These examples and many more stand as evidence of the ever-changing nature of the earth's surface. A geologist, forest ranger, or rock collector could provide fascinating information about local geologic interests.

Those living in the city are limited in availability of rocks for collection from natural settings, but a little creative effort can compensate rather well. Samples can be obtained from science supply catalogs or from local rock collectors. Possibly one or more students have collected rocks while on vacation that they would be pleased to bring to class and share with the group. As a group, the class might acquire an impressive rock collection by writing to friends and relatives. Trips to a local museum can provide meaningful geologic field trips.

Activity 3.1
HOW ARE SIZE AND DISTANCE SHOWN ON A MAP?

Materials Needed

- 8 1/2″ × 11″ paper
- Ruler
- Pencil

Procedure

1. Draw a map of your classroom. Be sure to include the furnishings, such as tables, chairs, bookcases, and desks.

2. Look carefully at your map. Compare it with the classroom. Do they look the same? Are they the same size?

3. If you mailed your map to a friend, what could you do to help your friend understand how big the room and the pieces of furniture really are? If others are doing this same activity, talk to them about ideas for including this information on your map.

4. When you think of an answer to step 3, fix your map so it will show how big things on it really are.

Teacher Information

A map is a representation of a portion of the earth, or sometimes all of it. This activity introduces a series of activities designed to help children understand how the earth, or portions of it, is represented in miniature form for observation and study. Depending upon maturity level and prior experience with maps, students might need assistance in deriving a suitable answer for the question in step 3. One solution is to use a scale, letting each centimeter or inch on the map represent a certain distance in the classroom. Any workable solution should be accepted. If those given are impractical, students can be led to "discover" the use of a scale through discussion and use.

INTEGRATING: Math, language arts, social studies, art

SKILLS: Observing, inferring, measuring, communicating, comparing and contrasting, using space-time relationships

Activity 3.2
HOW CAN YOU SHOW YOUR SCHOOL GROUNDS ON A SHEET OF PAPER?

Materials Needed

- 8 1/2″ × 11″ paper
- Ruler
- Pencil

Procedure

1. In Activity 3.1, you drew a map of your classroom and furniture. If you followed the instructions carefully, you included a way for your map to show the real size of objects on it.

2. Draw a map of your school grounds, including the schoolhouse, ball field, playground, swings, and all other equipment. Before you begin, review what you did for Activity 3.1. Use the same idea for showing the real size of things on your school grounds map that you used on your classroom map.

3. Compare your school grounds map with your classroom map. What is the same and what is different?

4. On your map of the school grounds, draw your classroom in the school building, showing it in its actual location in the building.

5. Could you draw all the furniture in your classroom on this map, just as you did on your first map? What is different? Why?

6. What changes does a map maker have to make in order to show larger areas on a map?

Teacher Information

The purpose of this activity is to cause students to expand the amount of area they include as they draw a map on paper. They should begin to get the idea that any area can be represented on a small sheet of paper. As the area increases in size, the scale must change, putting more actual distance into a given amount of space on the map. In discussion of steps 5 and 6, be sure students realize that the map maker must decrease detail as greater areas are represented.

INTEGRATING: Math, language arts, social studies, art

SKILLS: Observing, inferring, measuring, communicating, comparing and contrasting, using space-time relationships

Activity 3.3
WHAT CAN YOU LEARN FROM A SQUARE METER OF SOIL?

 Take home and do with family and friends.

Materials Needed

- Meter stick or measuring tape
- Small shovel
- Magnifying glass
- Ball of string
- Tongue depressors
- Paper and pencil
- Encyclopedias and other resources

Procedure

1. Measure off one square meter (or one square yard) of soil.

2. Mark your plot of ground by outlining it with string, anchoring your string at the corners with tongue depressors.

3. Select a place to begin, perhaps at one corner.

4. Write down all the things you can find within your square meter (yard), including each type of grass, weed, insect, rock, and so forth. Describe or draw the different types of plant and animal life.

5. Dig into the soil. Add to your list anything else you find, such as worms, more insects, roots, or rocks.

6. Pick up a handful of soil. Feel it and describe it on your paper. Is it hard, soft, spongy, moist, or dry? Does it pack into a ball when you squeeze it, or does it remain loose? Is it sandy?

7. Now examine your plants, insects, rocks, and soil with the magnifying glass and see how much additional information you can write down—things you could not see or did not notice without the magnifying glass.

8. Try to find out the names of some of the plants, animals, and rocks on your list. Use encyclopedias, field manuals, or resource people you think might know.

Teacher Information

We so often look without seeing. Students will be amazed at how much they learn from a tiny plot of ground—perhaps an area they have walked across, or near to, many times. Encourage students, especially those who show high interest in this activity, to select another plot and repeat the steps above. Suggest that the second plot be some distance from the first—at home, for instance. Compare information from the two. If interest continues, this activity could be repeated several times, with new information and new insights gained each time.

This could also provide an excellent opportunity to develop a study of how soil is formed from rocks and other materials (see Activity 3.4).

INTEGRATING: Reading, language arts, social studies

SKILLS: Observing, inferring, classifying, measuring, communicating, using space-time relationships, identifying and controlling variables, researching

Activity 3.4
HOW IS SOIL MADE?

 Take home and do with family and friends.

Materials Needed

- Rocks
- Sand
- Magnifying glass
- Leaves
- Soil
- Dishpan or bucket

Procedure

1. Examine the rocks and sand with the magnifying glass.

2. How are the rocks and sand alike? How are they different?

3. Each grain of sand was once a part of a rock and was broken off by natural forces. As the sand is ground finer and finer and mixed with organic material, such as decaying plant material, soil is formed. This process takes a long time for nature to perform.

4. Put a thick layer of sand in the pan or bucket.

5. Break up some leaves, or other plant material, into tiny pieces. You could even grind this material up between two rocks.

6. Mix the fine plant material into the sand. Use about the same amount of this material as the amount of sand you are using.

7. Compare your mixture with the soil. What likenesses do you observe? What differences?

8. If you can, set your mixture and soil aside for several weeks. Then compare them again.

For Problem Solvers: Do some research and find out what soil ingredients are essential for most plants. Get some seeds for a fast-growing plant.

Prepare three or four different soil mixes—with different amounts of humus, different amounts of sand, and so on. Predict which of these types of soil your plant will grow best in. In this case, your prediction is your hypothesis, or your best guess as to which will do best. Test your prediction by experimenting—by growing some seeds in each type of soil. Be sure that each sample gets the same amount of water and sunlight, so you can be quite sure that any difference in growth is due to the difference in the soil.

After the plants begin to grow, measure and record the growth of the plants at least twice each week. Make a graph of their growth and use your graph to explain to others what you learned about soil and plant growth.

Teacher Information

Soil begins to form when rocks and similar materials on or near the earth's surface are broken down by environmental forces. The substance that results from this action is called *parent material*. Parent material is broken down into mineral particles through a process called *weathering*. There are two kinds of weathering: *physical disintegration* (caused by such forces as ice and rain) and *chemical decomposition* (such as when water dissolves certain minerals in a rock). Through the centuries, organic material mixes with the parent material and the resultant matter resembles the parent material less and less.

Various environmental factors affect soil formation, including climate, land surface features, plants and animals present, kinds of parent material, and time. The mineral content of parent material helps determine the kinds of plants that grow in the soil.

Just as soil is constantly being formed, it is also constantly being destroyed by erosive forces such as wind and water.

Although this activity will not produce real soil, it will result in a soillike material and will provide a glimpse of nature's soil-making process. If circumstances will allow, let the mixture stand for a period of several weeks or months. Leaves break down quite rapidly, and the substance will appear more like soil than when first mixed.

Consider having students crush their own rocks by using other rocks or hammers. If this is done, however, be sure adequate protection from flying chips is provided, especially for the eyes. Also be cautious of possible injury to fingers in the pounding process. Sand can similarly be ground into powder, resulting in a more soillike mixture.

Other organic matter can be substituted for the leaves, or added to them.

INTEGRATING: Math, reading, language arts

SKILLS: Observing, inferring, classifying, measuring, predicting, communicating, using space-time relationships, formulating hypotheses, identifying and controlling variables, experimenting, researching

Activity 3.5
WHAT FACTORS AFFECT WATER EROSION?

Materials Needed

- Two identical erosion trays
- Sprinkler
- Two basins, such as plastic dishpans
- Water
- Several books
- Soil
- Leaves, sticks, and small rocks
- Paper towels

Procedure

1. Put an equal amount of soil on the two erosion trays.

2. Spread several leaves, sticks, and small rocks over the top of the soil in one tray.

3. Tilt both trays at the same angle and place the basins below the trays as illustrated. Sprinkle one quart of water over each one. First predict which tray will lose the most soil.

Erosion Trays

4. Use paper towels to filter out all the soil that was washed away in the quart of water. Was your prediction in step 3 correct?

5. Again place equal amounts of soil on the two trays. This time, leave the soil bare on each tray.

6. Lower one tray slightly and raise the other slightly. Which do you think will lose the most soil during a "rainstorm"?

7. Sprinkle one quart of water over each of the two trays and filter out the soil that is washed away. Was your prediction in step 6 correct?

8. Compare the amount of soil washed away in step 7 with the amount washed away in step 3.

9. What can you say about soil erosion in the mountains and factors that affect it?

10. Try to think of other ideas you could try to find out what might make soil erosion occur faster or more slowly.

For Problem Solvers: Where in your area is water erosion a problem? In your own yard? In your schoolyard? On a nearby hillside? Think of a way to estimate the amount of soil that is lost each year. Do some research and find out some of the things people do to control erosion. Which of these methods do you think might work best in the area you identified? What could you and/or your class do to help? Organize a plan to make it happen, and carry out your plan. Check on the area each time there is a heavy rainstorm and see how well your project worked. Try to think of something you could have done to make it even better.

Teacher Information

In this activity students will learn that erosion occurs faster on steeper slopes and that erosion is retarded by plant growth and debris.

The "erosion trays" could be as simple as two or three layers of cardboard. They could also be made from a sheet of aluminum or sheet metal. Old plastic dishpans could be used by cutting the sides down part way and cutting one end out. Cookie sheets can also be used.

For the sprinkler, a watering can designed for flowers will work well, or simply use a quart jar and punch several holes in the lid with a sharp instrument.

Let students devise additional erosion activities using the same equipment. For instance, they could get a small slab of sod from the edge of the lawn and test it for erosion. Try some of the loose soil with leaves, sticks, and rocks mixed in as well as lying on top of the soil. Compare sandy soil with clay soil.

INTEGRATING: Math, reading, language arts, social studies, art, physical education

SKILLS: Observing, inferring, measuring, predicting, communicating, comparing and contrasting, using space-time relationships, formulating hypotheses, identifying and controlling variables, experimenting, researching

Activity 3.6
HOW CAN ROCKS BE DISSOLVED IN WATER?

Materials Needed

- Small pieces of limestone
- Corrugated cardboard
- Plastic wrap or large plastic bag
- Piece of clear glass
- Rainwater
- Vinegar

Procedure

1. Make a long trough of the corrugated cardboard and line it with plastic.
2. Prop one end of the trough so that it tilts slightly.
3. If the limestone is not in small pieces, break it up with a hammer or with another rock.
4. Wash the pieces of limestone with clean rainwater and spread them along the trough.
5. Add clean rainwater very slowly, drop by drop, at the top of the trough.
6. Clean the clear glass well and place it under the lower end of the trough to catch several drops of water that have soaked through the limestone.

**Trough Lined with Plastic,
Pieces of Limestone, and Glass**

7. Let the water evaporate from the glass.

8. Examine the dry glass. What do you see? Is it still perfectly clean? If not, what is on it?

9. What if this same process occurs with mountains of limestone and millions of gallons of rainwater? What happens? What has this to do with the formation of limestone caverns?

10. Repeat the activity, using vinegar in the place of rainwater at step 5. If you notice any difference in the amount of material deposited on the glass, try to explain why.

For Problem Solvers: Have you ever visited a limestone cave? Find out about the one that is nearest to your area. Visit the cave if you can, but at least study about it. Ask a geologist or a rockhound how the formations are formed within the cave. Consider what you did for the above activity, and what you learned about limestone. Why is that important in understanding limestone caves?

Teacher Information

Water containing weak acids will actually dissolve limestone, as is witnessed by the formation of many caves and caverns, both large and small. Once caverns have been formed, water keeps dripping into them and the rock material comes out of solution, forming stalagmites and stalactites.

The dissolving process is speeded up as the acid content increases. This is demonstrated by the use of vinegar. The acid involved is mostly carbonic acid, formed when water dissolves carbon dioxide. Other acids are contained in some air pollutants and washed out of the air by rain. This is called acid rain, and it can be harmful to plant and animal life and water supplies.

INTEGRATING: Language arts, social studies

SKILLS: Observing, inferring, communicating, comparing and contrasting, using space-time relationships, formulating hypotheses, identifying and controlling variables, researching

Activity 3.7
WHAT IS CONGLOMERATE ROCK?

Materials Needed

- Dry cement
- Dry sand
- Variety of rocks
- Plastic-lined shoe box
- Water
- Stick
- Magnifying glass

Procedure

1. Put one cup of dry cement, one cup of dry sand, and one cup of cold water into the plastic-lined shoe box and stir with the stick. Be sure to mix it thoroughly.
2. Stir your rocks into the mixture.
3. Let the mixture stand for two or three days.
4. What happened to the mixture?
5. Take your mixture out of the shoe box and remove the plastic.
6. Use the magnifying glass to examine your mixture. Can you see some of the rocks you put in it? Can you see the sand?

Teacher Information

A conglomerate rock is made of various smaller rocks that have become cemented together by nature, quite like the block of concrete students make in this activity. For obvious reasons, the rocks used for this activity should not be from a rock collection that someone wants to keep.

A small conglomerate rock formed by nature would be an excellent visual aid to accompany this activity. A field trip to an area where students can find conglomerate rocks in nature makes an excellent learning activity. Students could also examine sidewalks, concrete walls, and bricks to compare and find evidence of the "conglomerate."

SKILLS: Observing, inferring, classifying, measuring, communicating, comparing and contrasting, identifying and controlling variables

Activity 3.8
HOW DO YOU START A ROCK COLLECTION?

 Take home and do with family and friends.

Materials Needed

- Hammer and chisel
- Canvas bag (or other strong bag)
- Goggles
- Egg cartons (at least 3)
- Newspapers
- Marker

Procedure

1. Take your hammer, chisel, and bag and gather a few rocks to begin your rock collection. Around the school yard, at home, or on the way to school are good places to look. Try to find rocks of different colors and textures, and with other differences that you can see or feel.

2. It will probably be necessary to break up some of the rocks in order to get the right size specimen, or just to allow a better view of what the rock really looks like. Put the goggles on before you strike the rock with the hammer, or put the rock in newspapers, a bag, or other covering to trap the flying pieces and avoid injury.

3. Sort your rocks into three main categories, as follows:

   a. Sedimentary: Have a layered appearance. Usually feel gritty and break easily.

   b. Igneous: Often crystalline appearance, never in layers.

   c. Metamorphic: Very hard, appear more crystalline than igneous rocks. Crystals of each mineral are lined up in bands or layers.

4. Label one egg carton "Sedimentary," one "Igneous," and one "Metamorphic" and put your rocks into the compartments of the appropriate egg carton.

Teacher Information

To add to an established rock collection, one might need to visit distant or hard-to-get-to locations, but the collection can be started anywhere. A stone quarry or area that has been excavated is an excellent location, but some very interesting rocks can often be collected around the yard at home, at school, or at the side of a road. Hillsides provide excellent prospects, as do stream beds. If rocks for student collection are not available in your area, try to find another source. For instance, students could write letters to friends and relatives in other parts of the country and ask for some small samples of rock common to their areas.

Students should be encouraged to collect rock specimens that are neither too large nor too small. The egg carton suggested for classification and storage helps in keeping size under control.

As students begin their rock collections, explain that it is very important to keep a record of information such as collection location, date, collector, and rock type. An easy way to do this is to put a number on each rock, then write the information with that number in a notebook.

SKILLS: Observing, inferring, classifying, measuring, communicating, comparing and contrasting, identifying and controlling variables

Activity 3.9
WHAT OTHER CLASSIFICATIONS OF ROCKS ARE THERE?

Materials Needed

- Rock collections in egg cartons from Activity 3.8
- Vinegar
- Masking tape
- Marker
- Piece of white porcelain tile
- Rock identification charts and books
- Paper
- Pencil

Procedure

1. Use the masking tape and marker to put a number on each rock in the igneous collection.
2. List the numbers of the igneous rocks down the left side of your paper. Leave space at the right for recording information about the rocks.
3. Use rock and mineral identification charts in various references and decide what you think each rock is. Record your findings on the paper.
4. Now follow these same steps with your sedimentary collection and your metamorphic collection.

For Problem Solvers: Find ways to expand your rock collection. Find opportunities to go to new places and look for rocks. If there are hills and canyons in your area, explore them. Be sure you don't take any rocks illegally, as from private property, without permission or from a state park or national park. Write letters to people you know who are in other parts of the country. You could get someone to help you find pen pals—people you don't even know. Trade small rock samples with them by mail. As you communicate with these people, tell them about your area. They will be interested to know what the land is like, what trees grow in your area, what kinds of birds and other wildlife are common, and so forth. Ask them to tell you about the area where they live. Report this information to your teacher and your class.

As your rock collection grows, try to identify your rocks. Talk to a geologist or to a rock hound. Check encyclopedias, field manuals, and other references. See how many different types of rocks you can find and identify.

Teacher Information

Before beginning this activity, students should have already collected a variety of rocks and sorted them into the three major categories, using egg cartons or other appropriate containers.

Having completed these preliminary activities, students should be prepared to make a serious effort to further classify the rocks in their collection. Encyclopedias and field manuals on rocks are excellent sources for identification charts.

INTEGRATING: Reading, language arts, social studies

SKILLS: Observing, inferring, classifying, communicating, comparing and contrasting, researching

Topic 4:   Ecology

TO THE TEACHER

Ecology is both interdisciplinary and intradisciplinary. It is interdisciplinary because it involves content from the biological, physical, and earth sciences, plus all areas of the social sciences. It is intradisciplinary because the ecologist attempts to use information from many sources to produce a unique field.

Many of the ecological problems we read about, see on TV, or hear on the radio are global in nature. Some are highly sensitive and fall in the political realm. National and international relations often deteriorate over ecologically-based issues. This section does not attempt to deal with moral, economic, or political issues. It deals with some basics of the science of ecology and attempts to help students realize their place, as individuals, in the ecological system.

The first portion of the area deals in very simple ways with nature's balance, food cycles, and food webs. The cycles of soil, water, and air are alluded to but not introduced formally. If you care to pursue these in greater depth, your library can provide ample resources.

People are introduced into an ecological system in this section. Liberties are taken with the term ecosystem to generalize it to apply to the student and his or her interaction with the immediate environment. Human interaction with the immediate environment becomes the focal point. Conservation, cooperation, and individual responsibility are emphasized. You may be tempted, as many are, to become preachy at this point; however, the effectiveness will be greatly increased if students are helped to discover these ideas on their own.

As is the case throughout the book, discovery/inquiry and verbal responses are emphasized. In this section, pictures, charts, and written work should be saved for a final, culminating activity (see Activity 4.20).

Many of these activities could be enhanced by the use of movies on nature and wildlife. Teachers of young children should be aware that some movies show predators killing prey and portray life and death as they occur in a true ecosystem. Be sure to preview the movies and use only those you consider to be appropriate for your students.

Try to include as much art, music, poetry, and aesthetic experience as you can. Opportunities for enrichment are almost limitless.

Activity 4.1
WHAT IS A SIMPLE PLANT-ANIMAL COMMUNITY?

Materials Needed

- 24″ × 36″ labeled poster of the figure on page 44
- 8 1/2″ × 11″ unlabeled copy of the figure on page 44 for each student
- Crayons
- Pencils

Procedure

1. Compare your picture with the one on the bulletin board. This is a basic grassland community. It has six important elements. As your teacher explains the function of each, color it on your paper.

2. Energy from the sun in the form of heat and light is the very first ingredient. Without it, nothing else could happen. Label and color the sun.

3. Air must be present in order for life to exist. Since air is colorless, write "air" on a blank spot somewhere below the sun.

4. Moisture in some form must also be present. How do you think this grassland is getting moisture? Label and show it in some way on your picture.

5. Good soil is necessary for grassy or woody plants. Soil has dead leaves and sticks (*humus*) in it. There are also small animals called *scavengers*, such as worms, bugs, and beetles. Scavengers feed on dead plant and animal materials in the soil and break it down into smaller parts. Tiny bacteria and fungi called *decomposers* further break down materials into minerals that plants need in order to grow. Color and label the humus, scavengers, and decomposers.

6. Plants of many kinds grow above the ground. They all depend on energy from the sun, air, moisture, and rich soil. In turn they remove carbon dioxide from, and release oxygen into, the air. They give off moisture. Most plants use energy from the sun combined with moisture and rich soil to produce food. They are the *primary producers* of food on the earth. Without them, other forms of life could not exist. Color the plants and flowers in your picture.

7. Your grassland community is now working. Save it for use later on.

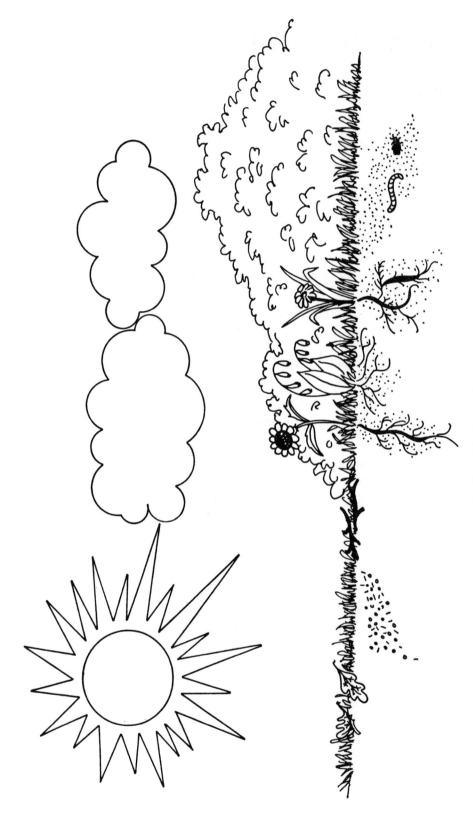

Profile of Grassland Community

44

Teacher Information

In the study of this portion of ecology we will consider groups or types of living and nonliving things interacting with each other as *communities*. When we add animals as primary and secondary consumers, we will then have an *ecosystem*.

Ecosystems can be as simple as a balanced aquarium in a classroom or as complex as an entire region, or country, or the world. Our studies will be confined to small communities and ecosystems to provide simple examples with which the students can relate.

As people are introduced into ecosystems, students will begin to understand how complex the problems can become.

SKILLS: Observing, communicating, comparing and contrasting, using space-time relationships

Activity 4.2
WHAT IS A POND COMMUNITY?

Materials Needed

- Student copies of grassland picture from Activity 4.1
- Unlabeled copy of the figure on page 47 for each student
- Crayons
- Pencil

Procedure

1. Compare the picture you made of the grassland community and the new picture you have.

2. This is a picture of a pond community. It is sometimes called an ecosystem. Label and color all the nonliving elements as you did in your last picture. If there are any new nonliving things, label and color them.

3. Use your picture from the last activity to label as many other similar things (grasses, scavengers, decomposers) as you can.

4. What new things are unlabeled and uncolored?

5. The animals in the picture do not produce food; they consume it. They are called *consumers*.

6. Animals that feed on primary producers (plants, grasses, and algae) are called *primary consumers*. Animals that usually feed on other animals are called *secondary consumers*.

7. In your picture, the small animals (shrimp, water flea, and snail) are primary consumers feeding on plants and algae. Label and color them.

8. The fish and frog are secondary consumers in this instance, since they feed on small primary consumers. Label and color them.

9. The snake is a higher-level secondary consumer that may eat either the frog or the fish. Label and color it.

10. The bird (in this case a blue heron) is an even higher level of secondary consumer because it may eat the fish, frog, or snake. Label and color it.

11. Whether an animal is a primary or a secondary consumer depends on what it eats, not on its size. The elephant is a primary consumer. A ladybug beetle is a secondary consumer.

12. Turn your paper over and draw a picture of the plants and animals in your classroom aquarium. Can you find both producers and consumers?

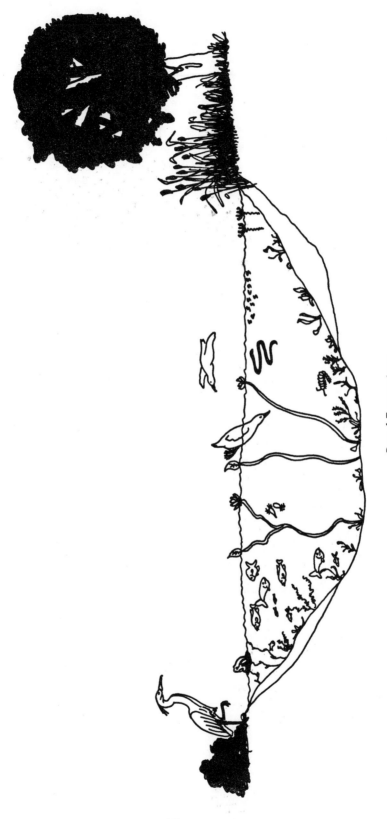

Pond Ecosystem

47

Teacher Information

If you do not have a freshwater aquarium or a good terrarium and have not developed one earlier in the year, this would be an excellent time. As students learn more about ecosystems, they will be able to have first-hand experience with a simple model.

As we add primary and secondary consumers to the model, the system becomes far more complex. Up to this point, the terms *herbivore* (plant eater), *carnivore* (animal eater), and *omnivore* (eats both plants and animals) have not been introduced. They are not necessary to the understanding of ecosytems.

SKILLS: Observing, inferring, classifying, communicating, comparing and contrasting, using space-time relationships

Activity 4.3
WHAT IS A SIMPLE ECOSYSTEM?

Materials Needed

- Picture of grassland community developed in Activity 4.1
- Pencil
- Crayons
- Pictures of animals shown in Figures 4.3-1, 4.3-2, and 4.3-3

Procedure

1. Figures 4.3-1 and 4.3-2 show animals that might live in a grassland community. Some are primary consumers and some are secondary consumers. Draw the ground animals on your picture of a grassland community. Color them.

2. Some birds are primary consumers. They eat berries and seeds. Others are secondary consumers who prey on primary consumers. Can you tell which is which? *Hint:* Look at their beaks and claws.

3. Now that we have added consumers, our grassland ecosystem is complete. However, we have two new kinds of animals. The smaller bird is a migratory animal who joins the ecosystem for a period of time when certain seeds or berries are ripe and then moves on to another location. On your picture of a grassland community, draw a migratory bird. Color it.

4. The second, larger bird is a predator. It preys on smaller animals. Notice its large, powerful claws and sharp beak. Some predators are migratory but many are permanent residents, depending on the food supply. Draw the predator on your picture of a grassland community. Color it.

5. Figure 4.3-3 shows some larger animals that might be found in a grassland community. Two are primary consumers. One is a predator, or secondary consumer. If you know what they eat, then you know which is a primary consumer and which is a secondary consumer. On your grassland community draw the new animals. Color them.

6. Now that you have developed both a pond and a grassland ecosystem, can you think of the reason why plants and animals live together and are dependent on each other?

Teacher Information

As consumers and migratory animals are added to an ecosystem, it becomes increasingly complex. Younger children may need to see colored pictures similar to the pictures of the animals they are asked to color. (Otherwise you may get purple ground squirrels!)

The existence of an ecosystem is directly related to energy and its transfer. The sun is the major source of energy. Lower forms of plants and animals spend most of their lives in producing and consuming energy. Reproducing the species, in many cases, is the only other function they perform. Some more advanced species do spend time in play.

The next activity introduces the concept of food chains and food webs, which form the basis for ecosystems.

SKILLS: Observing, inferring, classifying, communicating, comparing and contrasting, using space-time relationships

Figure 4.3-1

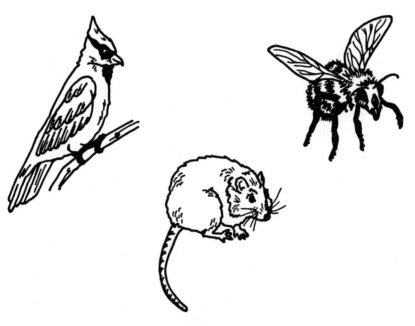

Figure 4.3-2

50

Figure 4.3-3

51

Activity 4.4
WHERE DO PEOPLE FIT INTO AN ECOSYSTEM?

Materials Needed

- 3′ × 6′ poster of the figure on page 53.
- Cutouts of plants and animals, such as Figures 4.3-1, 4.3-2, and 4.3-3
- Colored pencils
- Pictures of people, houses, stores, domestic animals, and so on
- Thumbtacks
- Drawing paper

Procedure

1. Study the picture on the large bulletin board. This is the way your community may have looked before the settlers came.
2. Identify the nonliving and living elements that make up the ecosystem.
3. Add a family to the system. What will they need to survive? Where will they get what they need?
4. Put a house and yard in the picture. Add a barn and barnyard. What animals will live in the barnyard? Where will the people get food? Where will they plant crops?
5. Add a second family with all the things the first family has.
6. What is happening to the ecosystem?
7. Add a third house, family, and barn.
8. Build a general store, church, school, and post office near the homes.
9. Is this still an ecosystem?
10. What changes could you make in it? Discuss planning as a part of urban and suburban change.

For Problem Solvers: How has the ecosystem of your community changed with time? Do you know how and when your town or city actually began? What was the area like before that? What animals and plants were common in the area? Which of these are no longer found there? Which ones were forced out of the ecosystem because of loss of natural habitat? Was it covered by forest, grasslands, marshes, or what? Why did people settle this area? Do you know anyone who has been there for many, many years? If so, ask them to tell you what they know about the early days of this community. Think of some questions you want to ask before you begin and write them down. Perhaps you could record the interview and share the information with your class. Ask at the public library for information about the story of your town.

Before you begin your search for information about your town or city, write a brief description of what you think the area might have been like, who you think the first settlers might have been, and why you think they came. Draw a picture showing what you think it might have looked like at that time. Compare your picture with what you learn about the way it really was.

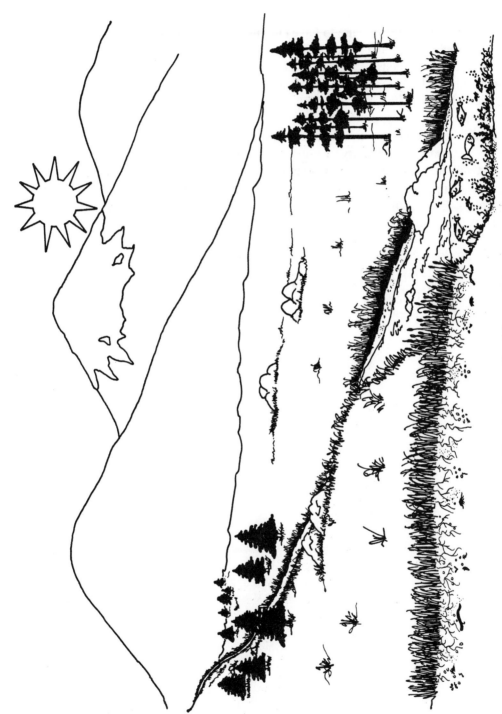

Grassland-woodland Ecosystem

53

Teacher Information

The figure on page 53 is a bulletin board developed from a grassland-woodland area. In representing more arid or humid regions, you can vary the environment and the people according to existing conditions. Be sure to have cutouts ready as you add people and houses.

Some teachers who like to sketch have used light pastels and drawn figures and objects in darker colors as the housing develops. The wild animals, fish, trees, and bushes will need to be removable or be covered by cutouts. Involve students in the development of these materials if possible.

If you live in a large city or suburban area, the bulletin board as shown in the figure could finally be covered by a tall skyline or rambling homes.

The purpose of the activity is not to show how people destroy natural ecosystems. Rather, it should help students understand that with civilization natural ecosystems will change and that planning can help society preserve, conserve, and restore many ecosystems in the world. People are second-level consumers. As such, they have responsibilities to ecosystems if they are to continue to be supported by those systems.

INTEGRATING: Reading, language arts, social studies, art

SKILLS: Observing, inferring, communicating, comparing and contrasting, using space-time relationships, formulating hypotheses, researching

Activity 4.5
HOW DO YOU FIT INTO A PERSONAL ECOSYSTEM?

(Class discussion)

Materials Needed

- 9″ × 12″ paper
- Colored pencils
- Ruler

Procedure

1. We have learned how the ecosystem of your community has changed with time. Whether you live in a very small community or a very large metropolitan area, many things have changed, are changing, and will change. In the center of your paper make a small picture of yourself.

2. Next to you make a picture of the people (family) with whom you live and any animals you own.

3. Place a rectangle around your picture. This represents the place where you live and is the first part of your personal "ecosystem."

4. Somewhere near your home, make a picture of your favorite outdoor place to play (yard, park, playground, friend's yard, or alley). This is a second portion of your personal ecosystem.

5. Make a picture of your school with your classroom located in it. This is a third part of your personal ecosystem.

6. Next, draw small pictures of other places where you spend time regularly (church, club, friends' places, grandparents' or other relatives' places).

7. Make boxes around all the pictures and draw lines connecting your "home" box with all the others. Estimate the amount of time you spend with each of the elements each week and write the time in hours and minutes if you can.

8. You are a second-level consumer, and this web of boxes and lines represents most of the "ecosystem" in which you live.

Teacher Information

You will probably need to use the chalkboard or overhead projector to show how to construct the web. Younger children will be unable to estimate time spent, and perhaps distance, but the size of the pictures they draw could substitute for length of time and importance to them. It is best not to "model" family size or structure by drawing in two parents, other children, and so forth.

The web, of course, is not intended to represent any type of true ecosystem. Its purpose is to provide focus for the following activities, which will be centered around individuals and their relationships to people and things around them.

INTEGRATING: Language arts, social studies, art

SKILLS: Observing, communicating, comparing and contrasting, using space-time relationships

Activity 4.6
HOW DO YOU LIVE AT HOME?

Materials Needed

- 9″ × 12″ paper
- Crayons
- Ruler
- Pencil

Procedure

1. Draw an outline of your home. Divide your home into rooms or living areas. Choose your favorite color and mark the space that belongs to you. If you share a bedroom, color your part of the room.

2. Use different colors to show places that belong to other individual members of the family.

3. Some spaces are shared with others in your family. Use different colors to show "community" areas.

4. Some animals who live together in communities within an ecosystem have rules that govern their own space or territory and territory shared with others. With other animals, most rules for community living are controlled by instincts—unlearned behavior that is beyond their personal control. Insect communities, such as bees and ants, live in a complex social structure controlled by instinctive behavior. In human communities, most behavior is controlled by thinking or reasoning—by rules.

5. On your paper make a small colored line to identify the territories (areas or rooms) in your home and write several rules for living and sharing in each territory.

6. Look at the rules you have written. Are they different for your personal territory, or territory that is shared by other members of your family, or guest territory if you have any?

7. Save this picture for a later activity.

For Problem Solvers: Some animals identify a certain territory and claim that territory as their own. They defend it against other animals of their own species. We say these animals are *territorial*. Read about bears, and especially about their territorial habits. Find out what other animals you can identify as being territorial. Are people territorial? Are you territorial? If so, in what ways do you show it? Share your ideas with your teacher and your class.

Teacher Information

The following series of activities will help the student identify his or her place in various communities. The use of terms such as family, community, and ecosystem may help students realize that, just as with other animal relationships, they too have rights and responsibilities.

A positive approach to the use of rules instead of instincts should help children understand that rules are necessary and helpful for survival, protection, and comfort.

Discuss and compare rules and family lifestyles with your class. Accept and positively reinforce differences. Help students understand reasons for the rights, responsibilities, and rules in their family community.

INTEGRATING: Reading, language arts, social studies, art

SKILLS: Observing, inferring, classifying, communicating, comparing and contrasting, using space-time relationships, formulating hypotheses, identifying and controlling variables, researching

Activity 4.7
HOW DO YOU LIVE IN YOUR CLASSROOM?

Materials Needed

- 9″ × 12″ paper
- Pencil
- Crayons
- Ruler

Procedure

1. Use your ruler to draw an outline of your classroom.

2. Locate and color your personal space in the classroom.

3. Mark and color your teacher's personal territory in the room.

4. Use another color to show the personal space of other students in the room.

5. Look around the room and decide what is shared space in your classroom community. Draw pictures of and color the shared territory. If there is any space not being used, leave it blank.

6. Think about the nonliving parts of your classroom environment. How do you get light, moisture, and air? Is the temperature comfortable for community living? Under your picture write a word or sentence to describe the nonliving parts of your classroom.

7. Since there are probably more members in your classroom community than in your home, what additional rules are necessary?

8. On your paper list several important rules everyone needs to follow in order to live comfortably with others.

9. Discuss and compare your picture and rules with those of other members of the class.

10. Save your picture for use in a later activity.

Teacher Information

In any community, rules work only if they are understood, accepted, and supported by each individual. Even very young children need to understand reasons for community rules. In animal communities, the rules of instinct have probably developed from survival through natural selection. People have extended rules far beyond the instinctive survival level. Customs, traditions, mores, taboos, and religious beliefs are often translated into some kind of pattern of rules or laws with which a society is governed.

INTEGRATING: Language arts, social studies, art

SKILLS: Observing, communicating, comparing and contrasting, using space-time relationships

Activity 4.8
HOW DOES OUR SCHOOL COMMUNITY FUNCTION?

(Class discussion and small groups)

Materials Needed

- Large chart paper
- Writing paper
- Pencils
- Portable tape recorders

Procedure

1. This activity may take several days to complete. With your teacher and other members of the class, make a drawing of your school on the chart paper. Show the classrooms and other spaces such as the library, lunchroom, auditorium, multipurpose room, offices, teachers' room, custodial areas, and restrooms. If your school has special features that you like, be sure to put them in.

2. Form small groups (four or five people) and choose an area (territory) of your school community you would like to study. List people you'd like to talk to and special things to look for in your area. Share the list with your teacher. Prepare some questions to ask about your area. Be sure to ask how students can help support this part of the school community. Ask about problems that are of special importance in that territory.

3. Make an appointment with the person in charge of the area you have chosen (librarian, principal, custodian, lunchroom manager, school secretary) and arrange an on-site visit. Be sure to take paper and a tape recorder so you will be able to report to your class.

4. After your visit, meet as a group and ask your teacher to help you prepare a brief report for the class. Include pictures and drawings.

5. Share your reports with the class. As other groups report, compare your findings with theirs.

6. Save all your material and notes for a later activity.

Teacher Information

Before you begin, be sure to discuss this activity with your principal and other members of the school staff who may be involved. Enlist their help in identifying special features and problems of their roles.

Students should realize that a well-functioning school community depends on the quality of each segment. A theme for this study might be "How do you help us? How can we help you?"

Be sure the students have specific questions to ask as they gather data for a report. As a part of the report, school staff members might be willing to visit.

Visualizing the whole school on a chart (step 1) may be difficult for younger children (some adults, too). Before you use the chart for class discussion, you may want to rule a light outline in pencil and use a black marker during the actual class discussion.

Save all material and notes for Activity 4.12.

INTEGRATING: Language arts, social studies, art

SKILLS: Observing, communicating, comparing and contrasting, using space-time relationships

Activity 4.9
HOW IS YOUR SCHOOL LIKE AN ECOSYSTEM?

Materials Needed

- Pictures of grassland ecosystem developed in Activity 4.1 (one per student)
- Large poster paper
- 9" × 12" paper
- Pencil

Procedure

1. Look at your picture of a grassland ecosystem. Remember the important nonliving and living elements in it?

2. How is your school like an ecosystem? On your poster paper, make an outline of your school building.

3. Instead of a sun to provide energy, make a circle above the building and call it "Learning."

4. Inside the building, write the name of the major consumer of "learning."

5. Inside the building, write the names of the major producers of learning.

6. Near the outside of the building, write the names of organisms (people) who help the producers and consumers.

7. Farther away from the building, write the names of nonliving things that help the producers and consumers.

8. Still farther away, write the names of migratory producers who help but are not a permanent part of the system.

9. Can you think of other things that need to be added to the ecosystem? If so, put them in.

10. Compare your school "ecosystem" with a grassland ecosystem. Which do you think is more difficult to keep balanced?

Teacher Information

This activity is suggested with apologies to any purists in the field of ecology. There are many micro ecosystems within the school building and on the school grounds. However, the purpose of this analogy is to focus on the students' role in a system that functions to assist them. It is not unlike farmers and some large industries that use resources to provide consumer products. Most of these industries recognize their responsibilities to the ecological system on which they depend.

The following activity will help students identify specific problems in the school "ecosystem" and devise methods to solve some of them.

This figure is a suggested model for your poster. Modify it to fit your own situation.

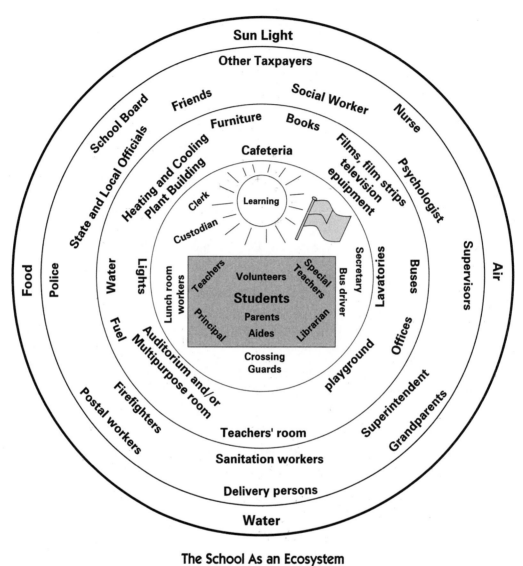

The School As an Ecosystem

INTEGRATING: Language arts, social studies, art

SKILLS: Observing, communicating, comparing and contrasting, using space-time relationships

Activity 4.10
WHERE CAN WE BEGIN?

(Introductory teacher demonstration)

Materials Needed

- Classroom wastebasket
- Tape recorder
- Blank recording tape
- Large photograph of Earth taken by astronauts as they stood on the moon

Teacher Information

This activity is suggested as a way to interest children in ecology as it directly affects their lives. It has proven successful in many classrooms. If you feel it is not appropriate for your group, just omit this activity.

1. Make a tape recording by someone with a deep, sonorous voice. This recording should have a few minutes of blank tape at the beginning. Place it in a battery-operated tape recorder, buried (but protected) under litter in your classroom wastebasket. Turn it on just before school begins or after lunch.

2. After the few minutes of blank tape, the wastebasket will say some of the following (adapt the taped message to fit your own situation):

   a. Call out several times (ask to be put on the table).

   b. Call attention to the kinds of things people are throwing away.

   c. Point out the condition of the classroom.

   d. Talk about hearing complaints from the garbage can where all school refuse is dumped; also the waste cans in the lunch room.

   e. Call the attention of the class to the photo of the earth taken by astronauts as they stood on the moon. Point out that this is all we have—this fragile globe on which we live; when it's gone, what do we do?

   f. Ask the students if they have ever heard of a food chain or ecosystem. Remind them that they are supposed to be consumers, not wasters. Consumers make contributions. Offer to tell them some ways they can help.

   g. Say, "Ms. or Mr. (teacher's name), tell everyone about the bulletin board you have on the wall."

INTEGRATING: Language arts, social studies

SKILLS: Observing, communicating

Activity 4.11
WHAT IS LITTER?

Materials Needed

- Garbage bags
- Large poster paper (one per committee)
- Glue
- Tongs (one set per committee)
- Clean cotton gloves (one pair per committee)
- Plastic-covered table

Procedure

1. Divide into groups of four or five.
2. Choose an area near the school building such as the school grounds, curbs (not street), vacant lots, or sidewalk.
3. Take a garbage bag and spend 30 minutes collecting all materials that are not part of the natural environment in the area. Use the gloves or tongs to pick up things that are sharp or dirty. (Don't collect or touch dead animals.)
4. After 30 minutes, return to class with the things you have collected.
5. Put everything on a plastic-covered table. Can you find ways to classify or organize them?
6. Use the poster paper and glue to make three-dimensional collages of the material.
7. Think of titles or slogans for the pictures.
8. Display them in your room and other parts of the school.
9. Wash your hands frequently during this activity.
10. The area you picked up is clean now. How could you keep it that way?

Teacher Information

This activity is regularly used in schools. It seems most effective when the goal is to sensitize students to litter and how easily it accumulates. The most important message should be that each bit of litter represents a careless, lazy, or thoughtless person. Many careless, lazy, thoughtless people produce an ugly, littered, and often unhealthy environment. Students should realize that they, as individuals, are responsible for the control of litter.

INTEGRATING: Language arts, social studies, art

SKILLS: Observing, inferring, classifying, measuring, communicating, using space-time relationships

Activity 4.12
HOW CAN YOU HELP AN ECOSYSTEM?

(Class discussion)

Materials Needed

- Group report materials from Activity 4.8
- Model of school "ecosystem" in Activity 4.9
- Newsprint
- Pencils

Procedure

1. This activity will take several days. Divide into the same groups you were in for Activity 4.8.

2. As a group, study the report you gave. Where do the problems you identified fit in the model of the school ecosystem?

3. If they are inside or close to the building, they are problems you can help solve.

4. Choose one simple problem and make a plan to help solve it (food waste in lunchroom, litter on school grounds, or similar problem). Discuss the plan with your teacher.

5. Contact the person in charge of the area where the problem exists and talk about your plan. Try to plan long-term solutions so the problem won't keep happening again.

6. Plan some way of reporting the results of your efforts.

7. What might happen if all the people tried to solve little problems in the "ecosystem" in which they live?

8. In Activity 4.6 you studied the place where you live as a "community." Could the things you did at school help solve problems in your home?

Teacher Information

Following through with a plan of action is the most important segment of this series of activities. Research has shown that information has little effect on behavioral change unless it is translated into tangible action. This is especially important for students in the early and middle years.

Emphasize that it is more important to do *something* rather than *everything*. Each individual can restore or preserve some small part of the ecosystem where he or she is.

Step 8 asks the students to examine their "home community." The extent to which you explore this topic should depend on your judgment of the circumstances where you are. Accept "home community" to be whatever it is to the student.

Teachers of young children who are not ready for committee work should continue with a focus on one area and one problem as identified in Activity 4.8.

INTEGRATING: Language arts, social studies

SKILLS: Observing, communicating, using space-time relationships

Activity 4.13
HOW CAN WE IMPROVE OUR ENVIRONMENT?

(Teacher-conducted activity)

Materials Needed

- Tape recorder and tape with harsh noises
- Very interesting short story
- Paper
- Pencil

Procedure

1. Prepare a tape of loud music or noise of some kind.
2. Select a short but engrossing story appropriate to the age level of your students. A short video could be substituted.
3. As you reach the most interesting part of the story, turn the noise on loudly enough to drown out the narration.
4. Turn the sound off and finish the story.
5. Discuss the following:

   a. How did you feel when noise intruded on the story?

   b. Noise is a form of pollution.

   c. Noise is a health problem. (Ear damage from very loud music; see "Hearing" in your encyclopedia).

   d. Much noise pollution is unintentional. Some cannot be avoided. Think of examples of both kinds.

   e. How can personal awareness reduce noise pollution?

   f. If you want to listen to music in public, how can you do so without disturbing others?

   g. In a discussion with friends, do you occasionally talk more loudly so people will listen?

   h. Think of five people you like best. Are they noisy, average, or quiet people?

   i. Are you a listener or a talker or do you do an equal amount of both?

   j. How can you reduce your noise level? Do you need to?

   k. How can you reduce the noise level around you?

   l. Make an action plan of things you can do now to reduce noise pollution.

Teacher Information

This activity is the first of several to help students become aware of problems we face as we live together in a "human community."

INTEGRATING: Language arts, social studies

SKILLS: Observing, inferring, classifying, communicating, using space-time relationships, formulating hypotheses, identifying and controlling variables

Activity 4.14
HOW CAN WE INVOLVE OTHERS?

Materials Needed

- Clean garbage can or large wastebaskets
- Plastic drop cloths
- Paintbrushes
- Tempera paints

Procedure

1. We have seen that noise pollution and litter begin with individuals. Most people will attempt to control these problems if they become aware of them and are given help. Divide into small committees and find a clean wastebasket or garbage can.

2. Plan a picture or slogan to paint on the can to attract other people's attention. Remember you want to attract attention and get people to use the garbage can.

3. Use bright tempera paint to decorate the cans.

4. Put them in special places in the school to attract attention.

5. With your teacher, discuss the possibility of challenging another classroom or even the whole school to a wastebasket-decorating contest.

Teacher Information

Simple, brightly painted cans are best. Be sure you have the approval of your principal and custodian before undertaking this project.

This type of activity will be most effective if the focus is kept on the individual, such as by using the word "you" in the slogan.

Perhaps your PTA would be willing to offer a prize for the best garbage can (or better yet, *all* cans).

INTEGRATING: Language arts, social studies, art

SKILLS: Observing, inferring, communicating, using space-time relationships

Activity 4.15
WHAT IS A WISE CONSUMER?

 Take home and do with family and friends.

Materials Needed

- Pictures of a modern grocery store or supermarket
- Paper
- Pencil

Procedure

1. With your teacher plan a trip to a nearby grocery store.
2. Ask the store owner to show you all the things sold in the store that could not be purchased 25 years ago, 50 years ago, and 100 years ago. Find out how many products are biodegradable.
3. Make a four-column list of things available 100 years ago, 50 years ago, 25 years ago, and today.
4. Look at the containers that new products come in. Ask the manager to tell you about them. Find out about sale dating.
5. When you return to your school, compare your lists. How have containers improved our lives? How has modern food handling improved our lives? What effect have these had on ecology?
6. Would you be willing to give up the modern products to have a cleaner environment?
7. Can you think of ways you could help with this problem?

Teacher Information

A grocery store or even a neighborhood fast-food establishment or delicatessen can be a rich source for studies in many areas. Ecology, economics, merchandising, service, and courtesy are topics to be studied in most stores. Old-time general merchandise stores still exist in small communities. The suburban shopping center is simply the enlargement and modernization of the same concept. In large cities, the relationship of people to the manager of the local deli may be similar to that of the people in a small town to the owner of the general store.

Someone in your class may have a relative who owns or works in a grocery store. Make a personal visit in advance and leave a written list of specific topics you would like covered during the class visit.

Although the major topics will be packing, conservation, and food handling as related to ecology, watch for other learning opportunities for return visits.

Emphasize that the great benefits of modern packaging and handling also create additional problems in garbage disposal and littering.

INTEGRATING: Language arts, social studies

SKILLS: Observing, inferring, communicating, comparing and contrasting, using space-time relationships

Activity 4.16
WHAT CHANGES HAVE HAPPENED WHERE YOU LIVE?

Materials Needed

- Two or three older people who have lived in your community for many years
- Paper
- Pencil
- Tape recorder

Procedure

1. Survey the class and identify two or three older people who have lived in your community for a long time.
2. As a class, make a list of questions you would like to ask about changes in the ecology of the region.
3. Contact the people and invite them to attend class and answer the questions. Be sure to ask them to bring old pictures or other items they may have to show. Emphasize that you are interested in changes in the physical environment of your community.
4. When your guests arrive, be prepared to ask specific questions about changes in ecology.

Teacher Information

Older people can be excellent sources of special information about your community. They often know of places in parks, yards of older homes, and even cemeteries where vestiges of the past still exist. Mutual lasting bonds are often formed from these visits.

INTEGRATING: Language arts, social studies

SKILLS: Observing, inferring, communicating, comparing and contrasting, using space-time relationships

Activity 4.17
DO YOU CONSERVE YOUR RESOURCES WISELY?

(Total class discussion)

 Take home and do with family and friends.

Materials Needed

- All clothing and other items from the school's "lost-and-found"
- Some item from home that is usable but that you have outgrown or no longer need or want
- Paper
- Pencil

Procedure

1. Look at the items in the school "lost-and-found" box. How many of the materials are still usable?

2. Why do you think they are there?

3. Can you think of a way to solve this problem?

4. Show the item you brought from home to the other class members.

5. Trade as many items as you can with other members of the class.

6. Perhaps some items left over could be used for another purpose.

7. Play the "What can you do with an old _____?" game. One person says "What can you do with an old _____?" and quickly holds up a leftover item. Everyone writes down as many things as he or she can think of in one minute. The one who has the longest list wins that item and has the chance to choose and hold up the next item. Continue this until everything is gone. At the end of class, if you really don't want the item you have won, give it to your decorated garbage can. It wants everything!

8. Return the lost-and-found items to the principal with any suggestions you have for their disposal.

For Problem Solvers: Many people have a lot of good-but-not-loved-anymore items. These things often remain unneeded and ignored for many years, while other people have need for those very things. Organize a project to help recycle unneeded articles. There are many things you can do. One possibility is to identify a central location where students can bring clothing and other usable items that are no longer needed, then present them to the local Salvation Army or other welfare organization. Perhaps the school could provide a place that could be used once a month, or whatever frequency seems appropriate. It might be appropri-

70

ate for information to go out from the school, both advertising the project and inviting those in need to come in at a preset time and have first choice on things that would be useful to them. Use your creativity, considering the availability and need of such materials in your area, and be sure to involve the school PTA.

Teacher Information

Your school may have another solution for lost-and-found articles, or it may have been one of the problems you studied earlier when you developed the school as an ecosystem.

The purpose of this activity is to help students become aware of how much we, as consumers, waste. "Use it up, wear it out, make it do" was the slogan that many people lived by a century ago. Today, in an age of plenty, it's easy for some to overlook the days before modern technology relieved much of the survival-level existence that was common in this country. In many parts of this country and in much of the world, survival-level living is still common. If you live or teach in such an area, this activity can have even more meaning.

SKILLS: Observing, inferring, classifying, measuring, predicting, communicating, comparing and contrasting, using space-time relationships, formulating hypotheses, identifying and controlling variables, experimenting, researching

Activity 4.18
HOW CAN YOU REUSE NEWSPAPER?

Materials Needed

- Newspapers
- Mixing bowl
- Wallpaper paste or liquid laundry starch
- Table, board, or cake pan
- Waxed paper
- Eggbeater
- Water
- Window screen
- Glass jar or drinking glass

Procedure

1. Begin with a piece of newspaper about 30 cm (1 ft.) square.
2. Cut or tear the newspaper into small pieces.
3. Place the pieces of paper in the mixing bowl, add a cup of water, and let it sit for a few minutes so the water will soak completely through the paper.
4. Churn the paper and water with the egg beater until the paper is broken up into very small pieces and the mixture looks something like oatmeal.
5. Add one tablespoon of wallpaper paste or laundry starch. (If the wallpaper paste or starch is in powder form, mix it with a little water before adding it to the batch.)
6. Stir the mixture well.
7. Lay the window screen on a table, board, or inverted cake pan.
8. Spread the mixture into a thin layer on the screen.
9. Lay a sheet of waxed paper over the mixture and roll a fruit jar or a drinking glass over it to squeeze out the excess water.
10. Carefully remove the waxed paper and allow the mixture to dry. It will probably need a day or two.
11. When the mixture is thoroughly dry, remove it from the screen carefully. You have made a usable product from waste material. This idea of reusing is called *recycling*.
12. Clean up the screen for use again.

For Problem Solvers: Organize a paper recycling program for your school. Find out about a company in your area that buys (or at least accepts) used paper for recycling purposes. Arrange for them to pick up paper at your school periodically, or for someone to deliver the paper to them. Get your teacher and principal to help you identify a location where all classes could deposit their used paper. The company that receives the paper might provide a collection bin.

Contact your local newspaper and tell them about your project. They might be willing to report it to the community.

Teacher Information

Much of the solid waste in the cities and towns of this nation consists of paper and paper products. Recycling of this material is an important industry and a worthy effort. Enough paper is recycled to save the lives of millions of trees each year. The paper produced by this activity is not exactly refined paper for your notebook, but it is definitely paper. Besides, it is done by the student and the process is quite like that done on a larger scale by paper industries.

INTEGRATING: Math, language arts, social studies, art

SKILLS: Observing, inferring, classifying, measuring, communicating, using space-time relationships, formulating hypotheses

Activity 4.19
HOW CAN YOU MAKE A WATER-TREATMENT PLANT?

Materials Needed

- Tin can
- Two shallow cake pans
- Board, slightly longer than the width of one pan
- Sand
- Small rocks
- Rubber or plastic tubing 45 cm (18 in.) long
- Metal puncher
- Several books or sturdy box
- Muddy water

Procedure

1. Punch two or three small holes near the bottom of the can.
2. Wash the sand and the small rocks and be sure the can is clean.
3. Put sand in the can until it is about half full. Add small rocks until the can is about three fourths full. This is the filter.
4. Place the board across the top of one of the pans and put the can on the board. The can should be placed so the drain holes in the can are off one edge of the board for free drainage.
5. Put the other pan on a stack of books or other support so the bottom of it is slightly above the top of the can. This is the settling basin.

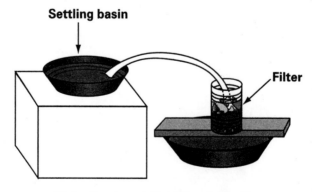

Water-Treatment Plant Ready for Use

6. Pour muddy water into the settling basin and let it settle for an hour or more.

7. Using the tubing as a siphon hose, siphon some of the water slowly from the settling basin to the filter and allow it the time needed to drain through the filter.

8. As the water drips out of the filter and into the pan, compare it with the water in the settling basin.

For Problem Solvers: Where does the water come from for your community? Is there a water-treatment plant near you? Do some research and learn what you can about it. How does the plant work? Does it use chemicals, filters, bacteria? How much water do they process each day? How long does it take to process the water? How does the treated water get to your home and school?

How and where is waste water from the community disposed of? If it is processed by a treatment plant, what could citizens do to make the task of the waste-water-treatment plant easier and more successful? After you have studied answers to these questions, discuss them with your class. If action of individuals is needed in making the treatment process more effective, try to work up a plan to get that started. Representatives of your class could even meet with the city council or with individual city officials to seek their assistance and advice.

Teacher Information

Before beginning this activity, explain to the students that many cities use lakes and reservoirs for their culinary water supply. This water must be purified in order to make it safe for drinking and cooking. Water-treatment plants are an important service to the people.

The water-treatment plant constructed in this activity is a fairly effective system for filtering muddy water. If it has been constructed properly, water from the filter will be clear. Have students try filtering some salt water with it. They could test the purity of the salt water by tasting it or by evaporating a small amount of the filtered water from a jar to find out if a salt residue remains in the jar. A similar amount of unfiltered salt water should be evaporated from another jar for comparison. Report what happens.

A field trip to a water-treatment plant or a sewage plant would be timely and valuable in connection with this activity. If this is not possible, perhaps a note home suggesting such an outing for the family would result in some of the students having the experience.

INTEGRATING: Math, reading, language arts, social studies

SKILLS: Observing, communicating, comparing and contrasting, using space-time relationships, formulating hypotheses, identifying and controlling variables, researching

Activity 4.20
WHAT HAVE WE LEARNED?

(Total-class activity)

Materials Needed

- Folders of materials developed during the ecology study
- Pictures, charts, and bulletin boards
- Resource persons

Procedure

1. As a class, plan an "awareness day" so you can share what you have learned with others.

2. Decide what you would like to show and how you will do it.

3. Who should be invited?

4. How can you involve and inform them?

5. To help you in your planning, consider the following ideas:

   a. Tell about the display, the notes, and the pictures you made as you studied ecology.

   b. Have a clothing (gloves, boots) exchange table.

   c. Make bumper stickers with "-ives" on them, such as "Dirt is abrasive, noise is intrusive, salt is corrosive."

   d. Display "new" things you have made out of "old" things.

   e. Create a "Lucy and Larry Litterbug" play. Record it on video tape and invite others to view it.

   f. Learn and sing some songs about ecology and a beautiful earth.

   g. Serve school-grown foods.

   h. Make litter bags and give them to others to use.

   i. Display "prize-winning" wastebaskets and garbage cans.

   j. Invite resource people from the community to attend and display some of their materials.

   k. Show parts of a favorite video you used during your study.

   l. Think of more ideas to add to this list. Do them!

6. When this final activity is over, be sure you leave your environment neat and clean.

For Problem Solvers: Investigate "Earth Day." Find out what it is, and determine ways to extend class activities to coordinate with national Earth Day efforts.

Teacher Information

An "awareness day" will help the students organize the materials and reinforce what they have learned during the study.

Involvement of other people, parents, and classes will require the cooperation of your faculty and principal.

INTEGRATING: Language arts, social studies, art

SKILLS: Observing, classifying, communicating

Topic 5:   Above the Earth

TO THE TEACHER

Suppose a small child at play on the beach at Kitty Hawk, North Carolina, had paused to watch the first flight of Orville and Wilbur Wright, in December 1903. Less than seventy years later, that same individual could have watched on television as the first man walked on the moon. The incredible and fascinating story of flight above the earth is introduced in this section.

To help students understand and appreciate the progress of the human race in the twentieth century, a brief background is presented as Activity 5.1. You are invited to read and discuss it with your class. Tape-record it for small-group discussions, have it read individually, or, if you prefer, choose an alternate method with your librarian or media specialist.

Learning to simulate controlled flight can be exciting and enjoyable. You may even find yourself helping to build a large cardboard mock-up of a pilot's cockpit with simulated controls. (If, as a result of these activities, you decide to fly a real airplane or space ship, we strongly recommend that you take additional lessons first.)

The following activities are offered to help you and your students learn about our remarkable progress in the quest to move into the unknown, and perhaps to challenge some of you to dream of what lies beyond.

79

Activity 5.1
WHAT IS THE HISTORY OF FLIGHT?

Materials Needed

- Story of flight

Procedure

Read this story and discuss it with your classmates.

"One small step for man. One giant leap for mankind!" Neil Armstrong's famous words as he took his first step on the moon marked an end and a beginning for man's desire to fly above the earth and beyond.

From earliest times human beings have seemed to want to follow the birds. We know there was at least one species of dinosaur that could fly (*pterosaur*) and an early ancestor of the modern feathered bird, called *Aechaeopteryx*. Myths, legends, and folklore tell of our continuing interest, and sometimes passion, to fly. A famous Greek legend tells about a boy named Icarus whose father gave him wings of feathers held together with wax to help him escape from his enemies. The wings worked, but while Icarus was flying he became careless and daring and flew too close to the sun. The sun's heat melted the wax that was holding the feathers together and Icarus fell into the sea.

For many centuries, people attempted to imitate birds by using their own muscles to power larger and larger wings. Near the end of the fifteenth century a famous artist and inventor, Leonardo da Vinci, drew plans and pictures of a manpowered machine for flight. There is no record that his design was ever constructed or tested.

For another 300 years, birds, bats, insects, a few fish, and squirrels (flying) continued to be the only animals capable of rising above the earth's surface. The attempts of people to rise above the earth, using muscles as power, continued to fail time after time. People were too heavy, and their arms and legs were too weak.

Late in the eighteenth century, a Frenchman named Joseph Montgolfier watched burned ashes of paper rising above a fire and suddenly had an idea. Although he did not understand why hot air rises, he made a small bag of silk, built a fire under it, and watched it fly away. Later, he and his brother constructed a large balloon, built a fire under it, and it lifted a man above the earth for the first time. Soon afterward, balloons filled with hydrogen gas were developed. The scientific principle of displacement use in "lighter than air" ballooning was discovered by a Greek scientist, Archimedes, in about 300 B.C.

Ballooning became popular as a sport. Some practical uses were developed for balloons, but because they were so fragile and difficult to control, their use did not become widespread. People still studied birds for an answer to practical flight.

Near the beginning of the nineteenth century, an Englishman named George Cayley discovered the first principles that would lead to controlled flight as we know it today. By watching birds, Cayley realized they work very hard to get into the air but once airborne, most were able to glide and fly using very little energy. Cayley became interested in how, for many birds, staying in the air required so little effort. He decided something must be holding them up. Using information about the pressure of moving air, Cayley was able to design and build the first successful glider that soared above the earth. Late in the nineteenth century, a German engineer named Otto Lilienthal developed methods to control glider flight, and controlled power flight became a possibility.

Before people could fly under power, they needed a simple, lightweight source of energy. Steam engines used in the nineteenth century were too heavy. Attempts to use them for powered flight always failed and often ended in disaster. The small, lightweight internal combustion (gasoline) engine seemed to offer a possible alternative to muscle power, which was not strong enough, and steam, which was not light enough.

At the beginning of the twentieth century, American brothers Orville and Wilbur Wright began experimenting with gliders on a windy beach at Kitty Hawk, North Carolina. On December 17, 1903, the first powered flight was made. Human beings had finally learned how to control and power flight.

Since that time, progress has been rapid. Air flight was adapted to transportation, communication, and even warfare. During the 1930's and 1940's a different source of power, rocket energy, was introduced and developed. For many centuries the Chinese, Greeks, and others had known about rocket propulsion but it was not until the middle of the twentieth century that it was seriously studied as energy for manned flight.

In 1957, the Russians put a small satellite, named Sputnik, in orbit around the earth. The first rocket-powered space flight came soon after.

For the next 10 years, step by step, flight after flight, test after test, human beings gradually climbed the ladder to the moon. Who knows what lies beyond?

Someday, some of you may follow the countless generations of people who wanted to fly. You are the astronauts, the explorers of the future!

Teacher Information

Have your students read this story or read it to them. You may want to come back to the story as you proceed through this section.

INTEGRATING: Language arts, social studies

SKILLS: Communicating, comparing and contrasting, using space-time relationships

Activity 5.2
WHAT IS A WIND TUNNEL?

(Teacher-supervised activity)

Materials Needed

- Variable speed fans
- Cardboard boxes with dividers (box must be larger than fans)
- Ruler
- Utility knife
- Paper

Procedure

1. For the following activities, you will need a controlled source of wind. Scientists and engineers use wind tunnels to test air currents around shapes they design. Remove the top of the cardboard box and lay the box on its side.

2. Measure the diameter of the fan and cut a hole in the bottom of the box about the same size. This will control the air from the fan and conduct it through the box.

3. Put the fan behind the box and turn it on.

4. Holding a flat piece of paper by the edges, move it in front of the box.

5. If the paper flaps upward, your wind tunnel is a success!

Wind Tunnel

For Problem Solvers: Study about wind tunnels. What does a real wind tunnel look like? How is it used? What kind of information do scientists and engineers learn from using a wind tunnel?

Teacher Information

For the following activities, you will need to borrow several fans and make several wind tunnels. Box fans are designed to be a type of wind tunnel, but because of their size, they often produce too much air. Eight- to twelve-inch fans with variable speeds are ideal. If they oscillate, there is usually an adjustment to stop the back-and-forth movement. Boxes with many small dividers, such as those made for pint or quart jars, are better than ones designed to hold gallon containers.

INTEGRATING: Math, reading, language arts, social studies, art

SKILLS: Observing, inferring, measuring, predicting, communicating, formulating hypotheses, identifying and controlling variables, experimenting, researching

Activity 5.3
HOW DOES SHAPE AFFECT LIFT?

Materials Needed

- 5″ × 7″ index cards
- Cellophane tape
- Pencil
- Wind tunnel
- Fan

Procedure

1. Bend two cards slightly in the middle and tape them together.
2. Put a pencil between them.
3. Hold the pencil supporting the cards in front of the wind tunnel. Turn on the fan.
4. What happened?
5. Use other cards bent in different shapes to see which works best.
6. Arrange your designs in order, from most effective to least effective, according to their tendency to <u>lift</u> in the air stream in front of the wind tunnel. Number them from best to worst.
7. Compare and discuss your findings with your teacher and classmates.

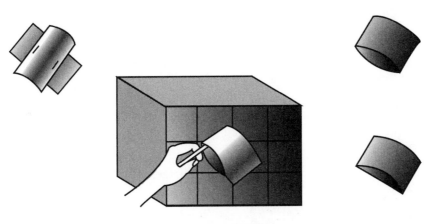

**Pencil and Cards Being Held
in Front of Wind Tunnel**

Teacher Information

As air moves over a curved surface, it goes faster, thereby reducing the pressure. A curved surface on the top of a wing reduces the air pressure above it, resulting in *lift*.

INTEGRATING: Math, art

SKILLS: Observing, inferring, classifying, measuring, predicting, communicating, comparing and contrasting, formulating hypotheses, identifying and controlling variables, experimenting

Activity 5.4
HOW CAN YOU BUILD A SIMPLE GLIDER?

 Take home and do with family and friends.

Materials Needed

- Strip of oak tag 20 cm long × 8 cm wide (8 in. × 3 in.)
- Two long, thin rubber bands
- Pencil

Procedure

1. Use the patterns in the illustration below to cut two wings from the oak tag.
2. Fold the ends of the tail up and use a rubber band to attach it near one end of the pencil.
3. Use the other rubber band to attach the wing near the opposite end of the pencil.
4. Slide the wing back and forth until the middle of the pencil will balance on the side of your index finger.
5. If your glider looks like the illustration, it is ready for the wind tunnel test described in the next activity.

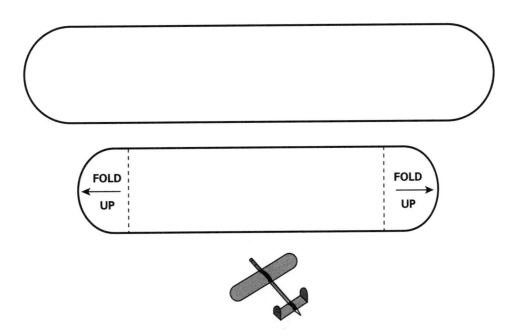

Wing and Tail Patterns and Completed Plane

Teacher Information

You may need to help the children attach the wings to the gliders. Use hexagonal-sided pencils so the wing and tail will align easily.

INTEGRATING: Math, art

SKILLS: Observing, inferring, measuring, predicting, communicating, comparing and contrasting

Activity 5.5
WILL YOUR AIRPLANE SOAR?

 Take home and do with family and friends.

Materials Needed

- Paper airplane constructed in Activity 5.4
- String 60 cm (24 in.) long
- Cellophane tape
- Wind tunnel
- Fan

Procedure

1. As they are being designed, new airplanes are tested in some type of wind tunnel. Use cellophane tape to attach the ends of the string to the front and rear of your plane.

2. Hold the string so your plane is level and balanced. You may have to change the position of your hand on the string and adjust the wing until it is.

3. Turn the fan on low speed and carefully move your airplane in front of the wind tunnel. What happened?

4. Twist the string to the right. Twist the string to the left. Move your hand so the nose of the plane turns up. Move your hand so the nose turns down.

5. How can you describe the behavior of your plane in the wind?

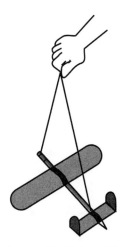

Airplane with String Attached

Teacher Information

If it is carefully balanced and aligned, the airplane will face the wind tunnel and maintain steady flight. Twisting the string will not turn the model because air passing the upright "rudders" on the tail section will hold it in line.

Lowering or raising the nose of the plane will cause broad, flat surfaces to be exposed to the wind, and it may spin out of control.

The purpose of this wind tunnel activity is to help children realize that gliders need more than a wing and a tail if they are to be controlled.

INTEGRATING: Math, art

SKILLS: Observing, inferring, measuring, predicting, communicating, comparing and contrasting, using space-time relationships, formulating hypotheses, identifying and controlling variables, experimenting

Activity 5.6
HOW CAN WE TURN OUR GLIDERS?

 Take home and do with family and friends.

Materials Needed

- Wind tunnel and fan
- Glider from Activity 5.4
- Scissors
- Ruler
- Newsprint
- Pencil

Procedure

1. Measure and carefully cut control surfaces in your glider as shown in the illustration below. Don't cut along dotted lines.

2. Follow the dotted lines to bend both rear sections of both rudders to the left. Hold your glider in front of the wind tunnel. What happened?

3. Try step 2 again, bending your rudders to the right. On your paper, draw pictures of the glider showing right and left rudders.

4. Straighten the rudders. Bend the left aileron down along the dotted line and the right one up. Hold your glider in front of the wind tunnel. What happened?

5. Reverse the ailerons and try it again. Make two pictures of your glider showing what happened when you used the ailerons.

6. Find the best combination of rudders and ailerons to make your glider turn smoothly.

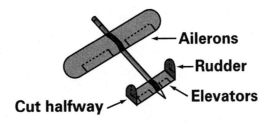

**Glider with Ailerons, Rudders,
and Elevators Marked**

Teacher Information

Rudders turn the glider left and right on a flat plane. Ailerons cause the wings to tilt or bank. With careful adjustment, the students should realize that a combination of banking with the ailerons and turning with the rudder will result in a smooth turn pattern.

INTEGRATING: Math, art

SKILLS: Observing, inferring, measuring, predicting, communicating, comparing and contrasting, using space-time relationships, formulating hypotheses, identifying and controlling variables, experimenting

Activity 5.7
HOW CAN WE MAKE OUR GLIDER GO UP AND DOWN?

 Take home and do with family and friends.

Materials Needed

- Same as for Activity 5.5

Procedure

1. Be sure the ailerons and rudder are straight. Test your glider in the wind tunnel to be sure it flies level and straight.

2. Remove your glider from the wind tunnel. Bend both elevators on the tail up.

3. Hang the loop of string attached to your glider over your index finger. Carefully move the glider in front of the wind tunnel. What happened?

4. Can you predict what will happen when you bend the elevators down? Try it.

5. Draw a side view of the glider showing what happens when you turn the elevators up and down.

6. Your glider now has the basic controls found in a real airplane.

Teacher Information

Elevators use wind to push the tail up or down, thereby causing the nose of the glider to move in the opposite direction. Tail down, nose up (climb); tail up, nose down (descend). Too much tilt in the elevators will cause a stall (nose too high) or a dive (nose too low).

The following activities are designed to see how well children understand flight controls.

INTEGRATING: Math, art

SKILLS: Observing, inferring, measuring, predicting, communicating, comparing and contrasting, using space-time relationships, formulating hypotheses, identifying and controlling variables, experimenting

Activity 5.8
WHAT HAVE WE LEARNED ABOUT FLYING?

Materials Needed

- Student sketches of gliders from Activities 5.6 and 5.7
- Pencil

Procedure

1. Study the pictures of the three aircraft illustrated. In each of the pictures, the pilot is moving a control that will make a change in the position of the airplane.

2. Use the sketches of your glider that you made in Activities 5.6 and 5.7 to identify each change.

3. Draw arrows on each figure showing what will happen to the aircraft.

4. Compare your answers with those of others in the class. If your arrows were correct, you are ready to try a solo flight.

Figure 5.8-1

Aileron Control Movement

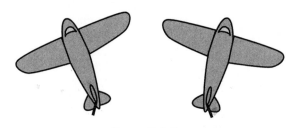

Figure 5.8-2

Rudder Control Movement

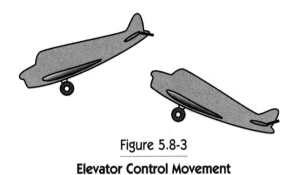

Figure 5.8-3

Elevator Control Movement

For Problem Solvers: Do you know how movements are controlled on a real airplane? Do some research and learn all you can about it. Look in your encyclopedia and other books, and try to talk to a pilot. How do the controls on a real airplane compare with the ones you have been using to control the movements of your glider? Share your information with your teacher and with your class.

Teacher Information

In Figure 5.8-1, the lowered aileron will force the wing upward. The arrows should point in the direction the aircraft is tilting. In Figure 5.8-2, the rudder forms a flat surface to push the tail in the opposite direction. Figure 5.8-3 shows the flat surface of the elevator turned down, forcing the tail up and the nose down, and vice versa. The figures show the aircraft in the middle of the maneuver. The arrows should point in the same direction as the aircraft appears to be moving.

INTEGRATING: Math, art

SKILLS: Observing, inferring, measuring, predicting, communicating, comparing and contrasting, using space-time relationships, formulating hypotheses, identifying and controlling variables, experimenting

Activity 5.9
WHAT AIRCRAFT WILL YOU FLY?

Materials Needed

- One piece of oaktag 20 cm long × 8 cm wide (8 in. × 3 1/2 in.)
- One piece of oaktag 8 cm long × 5 cm wide (3 1/2 in. × 2 in.)
- One piece of oaktag 5 cm × 5 cm (2 in. × 2 in.)
- Pencil with eraser
- Stapler
- Rubber cement
- Ruler
- Scissors
- Long, thin rubber band

Procedure

1. Shown here is a small picture of a larger "swept-wing supersonic" glider you can build. Look at the picture as you do the next steps.

2. Put the longest strip of oak tag across your desk. Put a dot in the center of the top, 10 cm (4 in.) from each corner.

3. From the bottom of each side, measure up 2 cm (3/4 in.) and put a dot.

4. Use your ruler to draw lines from the dots on the sides to the dot in the center. This is the leading edge of the wing of your glider.

5. From the center top, measure down 5 cm (2 in.) and put a dot. Draw a line from each bottom corner to the dot. If your outline of a wing is similar to the one shown here, cut it out. Cut ailerons in each wing 2 cm (3/4 in.) from the end, 3 cm (1 in.) long.

6. Use the larger of the other two pieces of oak tag to make the tail section. Follow the same steps as you did to make the wing. The center top will be 4 cm (1 1/2 in.) from each end. Measure up 2 cm (3/4 in.) on each side and connect the dots to make the front edge. Measure down 3 cm (1 in.) from the top center to make the center of the trailing edge. From this dot, draw lines to the lower corners. Cut your tail out and cut movable tabs in it for the elevators.

7. Put the small piece of oak tag under one half of the tail. Trace it, cut it out, and make a tab in it. This will be the rudder.

8. Staple the tail to a flat side of the bare end of the pencil.

9. Use rubber cement to glue the rudder upright on top of the tail.

10. Use the rubber band to secure the wing near the eraser end of the pencil.

11. Move the wing forward or backward until the tips of the leading edges of the wing will balance on your outstretched index fingers.

12. Without moving any of the controls, try your plane in a very gentle glide. Adjust the wing position until it glides smoothly.

13. Test each of your controls, one at a time, to be sure they work properly.

14. If everything works, you are ready to demonstrate how well you can fly.

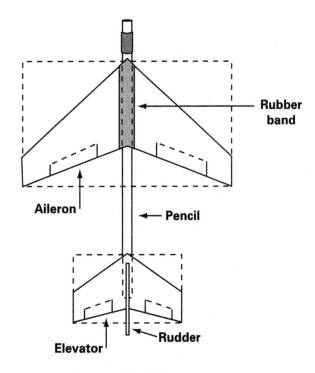

Swept-wing Glider

Teacher Information

Build and test a glider first before giving exact wing and tail measurements. You may prefer to increase the wing size. Exact measurements are not critical. The important factors will be balance and the ratio of wing and tail surfaces to weight. Bodies made of balsa wood or rolled oak tag weigh less but are not as sturdy and may need extra weight in the front.

If you, the students, or the parents have different "favorite" paper airplane designs, construct them. The only requirement should be that all aircraft have the three fundamental controls. Parental input should be limited to supplying interest, encouragement, and perhaps some assistance with the design, allowing the child credit for the major design and construction.

INTEGRATING: Math, art

SKILLS: Observing, inferring, measuring, predicting, communicating, comparing and contrasting, using space-time relationships, formulating hypotheses, identifying and controlling variables, experimenting

Activity 5.10
HOW WELL CAN YOU FLY?

 Take home and do with family and friends.

Materials Needed

- Glider constructed in Activity 5.9
- String 10 m (10 yds.) long
- Large ball

Procedure

1. Now that you have the knowledge and an aircraft, let's see how well you can fly. Choose a wide, flat area either indoors or out.

2. Put a large ball in the center of your area.

3. With one end of the string under the ball, make several spirals around the ball with the string. (See the illustration below.)

4. The spirals are your landing area, and the ball is your target.

5. Stand at least 10 meters (10 yards) away and try to land your airplane near the target. Remember, you should analyze each flight and make adjustments in your controls for the next flight.

6. Each time you hit the target, move back 5 meters (5 yards) and try again.

7. Have your teacher time you for 10 minutes.

8. At the end of the time, the pilots who are standing the greatest distance away are the "aces."

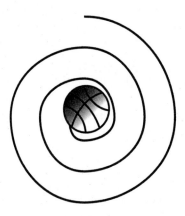

Target and Landing Area

Teacher Information

This "just-for-fun" activity should help to motivate students to prepare for the skill and creativity needed for Activities 5.11 and 5.12.

INTEGRATING: Math, art

SKILLS: Observing, inferring, measuring, predicting, communicating, comparing and contrasting, using space-time relationships, formulating hypotheses, identifying and controlling variables, experimenting

Activity 5.11
CAN YOU CREATE AN AIRPLANE OF A NEW DESIGN?

Materials Needed

- Oaktag
- Construction paper
- Writing paper
- Pencil with eraser
- Stapler
- Rubber cement
- Ruler
- Scissors
- Long, thin rubber bands

Procedure

1. Now that you have constructed airplanes, tested them, and learned some ways to control the flight pattern, create your own airplane design.
2. Draw your airplane design on paper, then get the materials you need and build it.
3. Your airplane may look very different from anything you have seen. It might surprise even you to find out what it really turns out to be. Still, you will benefit from what you have learned about controlling movement in flight.
4. Work with a partner if you wish.
5. When you are finished, display your airplane with those of the rest of your class. Have each person share his or her airplane and explain what special things the airplane is designed to do.

Teacher Information

This is an opportunity for students to apply what they have learned about airplanes in a creative way. When the finished products are ready, it will be a good time to invite other classes, parents, and others to come and see what students have made. If it can be arranged for each student to stay with his or her model during display time, it would be a valuable experience for the students to explain their design to visitors.

INTEGRATING: Math, language arts, art

SKILLS: Observing, classifying, measuring, predicting, communicating, comparing and contrasting, identifying and controlling variables, experimenting

Activity 5.12
HOW WILL YOU DESIGN AN AIRPLANE FOR A SPECIAL TASK?

Materials Needed

- Oaktag
- Construction paper
- Writing paper
- Pencil with eraser
- Stapler
- Rubber cement
- Ruler
- Scissors
- Long, thin rubber bands

Procedure

1. Prepare for a contest in airplane design.

2. First, decide what you want the airplanes to be specialized for: distance, accuracy at hitting a target, banking left, banking right, flying loops, or what.

3. Decide whether you are going to work in teams of two, small groups, individually, or if all are to decide for themselves.

4. Draw out your design on paper.

5. Get the materials you need and construct your airplane to the design you drew.

6. When everyone is finished, test all the airplanes to see which one is best at the specialization that was selected.

7. Examine the differences carefully and find out why one particular design was best, so everyone can learn from it.

8. Repeat the activity. As a group, decide whether to target the same specialization or to choose a new one.

9. Always remember to learn from each other, as you see certain design characteristics that seem to work better than others.

Teacher Information

This is another opportunity for students to apply what they have learned about airplanes in a creative way. Emphasize the importance of being supportive with each other, and learning from each other. The person who learns the most, and does the best job of helping others to learn, is the winner in ways that matter most of all.

A visit from a pilot (with visuals), a movie, or a field trip to an airport would be appropriate enrichment activities. The next series of investigations will help us begin a space adventure.

INTEGRATING: Math, language arts, art

SKILLS: Observing, classifying, measuring, predicting, communicating, comparing and contrasting, identifying and controlling variables, experimenting

Topic 6:   Beyond the Earth

TO THE TEACHER

The rapid explosion of space technology has provided an overwhelming amount of new information to astronomers. As you read this page, hundreds of satellites and controlled space vehicles are beaming messages, pictures, and other information about our neighbors in space. At the same time, other satellites are studying the earth and communicating new information about the weather, topography, temperature, and other features of our home planet. Astronomy and the resultant technology are on the growing edge of scientific knowledge.

Many of the numbers, distances, temperatures, and figures that we learn today will change tomorrow. If you ask students the number of planets and they say eight or ten instead of the traditional nine, think before marking them wrong. By many criteria, Jupiter can be classified as a sun and many astronomers believe there are planets beyond Pluto in our solar system.

And what of intelligent life in the universe? Many astronomers believe it is just a matter of time until we are in contact. Time is related to speed, distance, and space in ways few of us can even comprehend.

In this rapidly changing field of knowledge, be wary of teaching facts as absolute. Much information is tentative and changing.

As they begin to sense the incredible order and grandeur of the universe, your students will stand in awe and wonder. We invite you to direct the following activities toward that goal.

National Geographic (December 1969) produced exceptionally fine coverage and photographs of the first manned moon landing and exploration. Included was a small phonograph record narrated by astronaut Frank Borman, telling of the Apollo flights that led to the magnificent achievement. Neil Armstrong's first words as he stepped on the moon are recorded. This particular issue of *National Geographic* is strongly recommended, especially for students in grades 4–8. Check with your media center or public library.

Activity 6.1
WHAT DOES OUR EARTH LOOK LIKE?

(Partners and total-group activity)

Materials Needed

- Globe of the earth
- Pencil
- Newsprint
- Color photographs of the earth taken from the moon

Procedure

1. Pretend you are an astronaut and have just landed on the moon. You are on the side facing the earth. Choose a partner and describe how the earth looks from your position. Have your partner record words that tell what you think you would see.

2. Examine the globe in your classroom. It is a ball-shaped map of the earth. Can you think of any ways your view from the moon might be different from your view of the globe in your classroom?

3. Your teacher has actual photographs of the earth that were taken by astronauts from the moon. Discuss with your teacher and the rest of the class ways the globe is like and unlike photos of the earth.

Teacher Information

This introductory activity may be omitted if students are already familiar with photographs of the earth taken from space. The purpose of this activity is to introduce the globe as a fairly accurate model of the earth's surface.

In photos, clouds will often cover large portions of the earth's surface. Complete storm systems are often visible. Contrasting colors of land and water can be seen clearly. The atmosphere around the earth cannot be seen except where clouds are present. The blue sky we see from the surface of the earth is due to scattering and absorption of different wavelengths of light as the sun's light travels through the earth's atmosphere.

Photographs of the earth taken from the moon are available in encyclopedias, periodicals (especially *National Geographic*), library books after 1969, and probably your school media center.

INTEGRATING: Language arts

SKILLS: Observing, inferring, communicating, comparing and contrasting

Activity 6.2
HOW DOES THE EARTH MOVE?

(Total-group activity)

 Take home and do with family and friends.

Materials Needed

- Large playground ball
- Axis-mounted globe of the earth
- Small pieces of sticky note paper

Procedure

1. Today we are going to begin the construction of a model of the sun and some of the large objects in orbit around it. Place the playground ball on a table near the center of the room.

2. Observe the globe. Notice it is attached to the mount at two points. These are the ends of an imaginary line running through the center of the earth, called the axis. We call these two points the North and South Poles.

3. Make the playground ball spin. As it spins, can you find the axis (point around which it spins)? What happens when it begins to slow down? Can you think of reasons why it slows down?

4. Spin the globe. Is its movement different from that of the ball? Explain.

5. The turning of the earth on its axis is called rotation. It turns completely around once in every 24 hours.

6. Use the globe to locate the place where you live. Put a small sticky note paper on that spot.

7. Put the globe in a corner of the room and pretend you are standing on the paper trying to see the playground ball (sun) in the center of the room.

8. Slowly rotate (turn) the globe completely around. If you are standing on the globe and it is rotating, how much of the time will you be able to see the sun (playground ball)? Can you see what makes night and day where you live?

Teacher Information

The concept that the earth rotates on its axis may seem simple to the adult mind, but it is extremely important to the whole idea of movement and change in our solar system and the universe. If we rely on past experience of movement and our powers of observation, simple logic may convince us that the earth stands still and the sun moves around it. For centuries some influential philosophers and astrologers in the Western world held this belief (See "Ptolemaic Theory" in the encyclopedia). In the sixteenth century, Copernicus, Kepler, and Galileo discovered the correct principles of solar movement.

At the equator the earth rotates at a speed of approximately 1,000 miles per hour. We do not sense any movement because everything, including our atmosphere, is moving together at a smooth pace. On the earth we have learned to judge speed by the rush of wind, vibration, sound, abrupt changes in gravity and speed, and the rate at which we pass reference points, such as fence posts. In space, with the exception of inertia, none of the usual phenomena associated with movement are present. For this reason, astronauts traveling in orbit around the earth at over 17,000 miles an hour feel no sensation of movement. From the moon, the earth would appear to be rotating. You should be aware that the exact rotation time of the earth is slightly less than 24 hours. Scientists correct for this by occasionally adding one second to the official worldwide standard time kept in Greenwich, England.

The next activity develops the concepts of the earth's revolution around the sun and why seasons occur.

SKILLS: Observing, inferring, communicating, comparing and contrasting, using space-time relationships, formulating hypotheses

Activity 6.3
HOW DOES THE EARTH TRAVEL?

(Total-group activity)

Materials Needed

- Axis-mounted globe of the earth
- Large playground ball
- One copy of the figure on page 109 for each student

Procedure

1. In addition to *rotating* on its axis once very 24 hours, the earth also *revolves* or travels around the sun, once a year (365 1/4 days). Hold the globe in your hand and spin it evenly (not too fast) while you walk completely around the playground ball. You have now performed the basic movements the earth and other planets make in the solar system. It took thousands of years for people to make this basic discovery.

2. The earth is kept in the same path around the sun because of the attraction of the sun's gravity. The path an object follows as it revolves around another object is called an *orbit*. Study the drawing your teacher has given you. During a yearly trip around the sun, the earth is shown in four positions in its *orbit*. Notice that the earth travels in a *counterclockwise* direction.

3. Observe the globe and the diagram of the earth revolving around the sun. Notice that the axis upon which the earth rotates is not upright but tilted approximately 23.5°. As it revolves around the sun, the north end of the earth's axis continues to point toward a relatively stationary object in the sky called the North Star. Notice in the diagram that the axis in all four drawings of the earth would come together (converge) at a distant point if you continued to draw them in a straight line. This would be the location of the North Star.

4. The North and South American continents are shown on all four diagrams of the earth. Observe that the unchanging tilt of the earth causes the North American continent to tilt toward and away from the direct rays of the sun in its annual progress. When the continent is tipped toward the sun, the more direct rays produce more heat and cause summer. Tilting away from the direct rays causes winter. Twice a year the angle of the rays is equal. These are the times of the *vernal equinox* (spring) and the *autumnal equinox* (autumn, or fall). The beginnings of winter and summer come at opposite ends of the earth's orbit, and are called summer and winter *solstice*.

For Problem Solvers: As you do this activity, think about what causes day and night. If the earth goes around the sun once each year, why does the sun appear to go around the earth every day?

When you think you have the answer to this question, discuss your ideas with your group. Listen to their ideas and see if you agree. As a group, present your ideas to your teacher and to the class. Demonstrate your ideas with globe models of the earth and sun. If there are disagreements, do some more research and find the right answers. Use your model to also demonstrate what causes the seasons to change.

Teacher Information

Most students will be able to understand the simple solar mechanics of rotation and revolution (steps 1 and 2).

The tilt of the earth and its effect on seasonal change requires abstract visualization and formal thinking, for which many elementary students may not be developmentally ready. The diagram may help concrete thinkers to visualize seasonal change, but many may continue to believe that the earth is closer to the sun in the summer and farther away in winter, although the opposite is true in our hemisphere.

A Note to Teachers of Young Children

The simple ideas of rotation and revolution can be developed through role playing. Have one child be the sun and stand in the center of the room. Have another be the earth and slowly walk (revolve) around the "sun" while turning around (rotating) at the same time. Point out that in order to be accurate, the "earth" child would need to turn around (rotate) 365 1/4 times each trip around the sun.

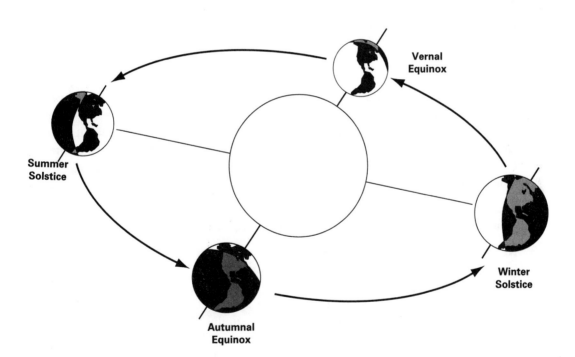

Earth's Orbit Around the Sun

INTEGRATING: Reading, language arts, social studies

SKILLS: Observing, inferring, communicating, comparing and contrasting, using space-time relationships, formulating hypotheses

Activity 6.4
WHAT PATHS DO EARTH AND SIMILAR OBJECTS FOLLOW?

(Individual and small-group activity)

Materials Needed

- Rubber ball attached to elastic 1 m (1 yd.) long (or paddleball toy)
- 8- or 12-ounce plastic foam cup
- 45 cm × 45 cm (18 in. × 18 in.) or larger cardboard box for base
- 45 cm × 45 cm (18 in. × 18 in.) unlined white paper
- String 20 cm (8 in.) long
- String 60 cm (24 in.) long
- Thumbtacks or pushpins
- Sharp pencil
- Colored pencils

Procedure

1. Before the sixteenth century most people in the Western world (Europe) believed the earth stood still and the sun, moon, and stars all revolved around it. Copernicus was the first man to state the idea that the sun was in the center of a system and that the earth and some other bodies revolved around it. The path of the earth around the sun was called an *orbit*. Place your paper on the cardboard box. In the center of your paper make a picture of the sun.

2. Using a thumbtack, attach one end of the 20-cm (8-in.) length of string to the center of your picture of the sun. Tie your pencil to the other end of the string.

3. Keeping the string *taut* at all times, use the point of your pencil to draw a circle around the sun on the paper. Draw a picture of the earth on the circle. This model is similar to the idea Copernicus had of the earth's path around the sun. A few stars, called *planets* (Greek word meaning "wandering star"), also moved through the sky in strange ways. Copernicus believed these "stars" were bodies similar to earth and also moved in circles around the sun.

4. Soon after Copernicus made his ideas known, a mathematician named Johannes Kepler observed that the actual movement of the earth and other planets did not quite agree with Copernicus' theory. Using his mathematical knowledge, Kepler changed the round paths or orbits to slightly *elongated* orbits called *ellipses*. There are several ways you can draw an ellipse. One of the easiest is to use the mouth of a plastic foam cup. Put the cup, mouth down, on a piece of paper. With your pencil, move the point around the mouth to make a circle. Now hold the cup in its center with your thumb on one side and your fingers on the other. Gently squeeze until the mouth of the cup is no longer round.

With your pencil trace the mouth. Can you see how a circle can be elongated to form an ellipse?

5. If you have ever played with a small ball attached to an elastic, you have probably accidentally or on purpose made an ellipse. Hold the end of the elastic or paddle so the ball nearly touches the floor. Slowly move your hand or the paddle around and around until the ball is moving in a circular path. Now, gradually change the motion of your hand so it moves back and forth rather than in a circle. Observe the path of the ball. Describe the changes you see.

6. You can draw an ellipse over the first picture model of the sun and earth you drew on the large piece of paper (steps 2 and 3 above). Tie the ends of the 60-cm (24-in.) string together. Press two thumbtacks halfway into the paper and the cardboard box 20 cm (8 in.) apart in a line across the picture of the sun. Place the circular string loosely under the two thumbtacks. With your pencil, stretch the string taut under the thumbtacks. Keep the string taut but allow it to make a circle. What happened? Can you change the shape of your ellipse by moving one thumbtack? What happens if you move both thumbtacks? Kepler discovered that the planets in our *solar* (sun) *system* move in paths that are slightly elliptical. In later times, other members of our solar system, such as some comets, were found to have very elongated elliptical orbits.

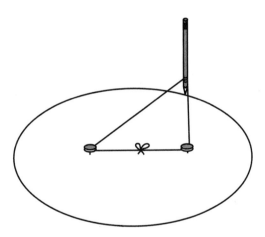

Apparatus for Making an Elliptical Orbit

For Problem Solvers: Get the encyclopedias and study about the discoveries of Copernicus, Kepler, and Galileo. Find out how they agreed or disagreed on their theories of movements within the solar system. Why were people so slow to accept the theories of these scientists? Did all scientists of the time agree with them? Looking into the sky, the sun clearly appears to go around the earth. How long do you think it would have taken you to discover that it isn't that way at all? How do you think you would have gone about the task of studying these movements hundreds of years ago? Discuss your ideas with others in your group.

Teacher Information

The theory of Copernicus, modified by Kepler and later verified by Galileo, did not electrify the scientific community in the seventeenth century. Galileo was convicted of heresy, partly because of his strong support of the Copernican model of the solar system. The purpose of this activity is to emphasize that objects in the solar system travel in elliptical, and not round, orbits as are often pictured. You may be able to communicate this concept by using one or two, rather than all, of the activities. It is important for students to understand that orbital paths vary. The paths of the two outermost known planets, Neptune and Pluto, cross each other. Halley's Comet, which passed Earth in 1985 and 1986, is in a greatly elongated orbit that carries it beyond Pluto during its 75-year journey.

INTEGRATING: Reading, language arts, social studies

SKILLS: Observing, inferring, communicating, using space-time relationships, formulating hypotheses, researching

Activity 6.5
HOW DO MAN-MADE SATELLITES HELP US?

(Total-group activity)

Materials Needed

- Globe of the earth
- 1-cm (1/4-in.) ball of aluminum foil
- Bits of gummed paper
- Pencil

Procedure

1. Attach a small piece of gummed paper on the globe and mark the spot where you live and, with the point of your pencil, make a tiny dot on the paper. If your globe is an average size, 30–40 cm (12–16 in.), you, your school, and your community could fit within the tiny dot on the paper. In fact, the dot represents the greatest portion of the earth's surface that can be seen from any given location on the earth. Can you think of ways to help you see a greater distance?

2. Since television and some other communication signals travel in a straight line, they can travel only short distances without being relayed (passed on) in some way. Hold an aluminum foil ball above the spot you marked on your globe. Have someone slowly turn the globe while you keep the foil ball directly above the mark. Notice that the foil ball is moving at a speed that matches the rotation of the earth. This is the way communication satellites work. If you were very small, standing at the marked point, would the foil ball appear to be moving? Why? Look at Figure 6.5-1. With the ball acting as a reflector, television signals could be sent to you from a great distance away, in the same way that a mirror reflects light.

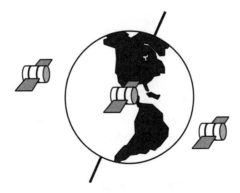

Figure 6.5-1

Earth with Communication Satellites in Orbit

3. Look at Figure 6.5-2. The orbit of this satellite is elliptical. At one point, the satellite comes very near the earth. This is called the *perigee*. The greatest distance a satellite moves away from a parent body is called the *apogee*.

Figure 6.5-2

Earth with Satellite in Sharp Ellipse

For Problem Solvers: Study about how satellites are used today. Make a list of all the ways they are used that you can find. How far above the earth are the orbits of satellites? Why are they at that altitude? Are they all the same distance from the earth's surface? Are our lives better, because of satellites, or just more complicated? What do you think? Discuss your ideas with your teacher and other students.

Teacher Information

Orbits of satellites launched in space by NASA vary according to the purpose of the satellite. Some are in "stationary" orbits that are almost round and almost exactly match the speed of the earth's rotation. These communication satellites appear to "hang" stationary in the sky, and they reflect and relay television signals around the earth. Telecommunications for the entire world depend on these satellites (see Figure 6.5-1). Some satellites are put in greatly elongated orbits in order to come very near the earth at a specific point. Satellites are also used to relay weather information, specific geographic data (including geothermal and faulting), and for military purposes.

In an elliptical orbit, the point at which a satellite is closest to its parent body is called the *perigee*. The point furthest from the parent body is called the *apogee* (Figure 6.5-2). There have been thousands of man-made satellites launched in orbit around the earth since 1957. Many of them are no longer useful. See the encyclopedia and library books for further information.

INTEGRATING: Math, reading, language arts, social studies

SKILLS: Communicating, using space-time relationships, researching

Activity 6.6
HOW IS OUR MOON A NATURAL SATELLITE?

(Total-group activity)

Materials Needed

- Pencil
- Paper
- One copy of "Do You Know This About the Moon?" for each student

Procedure

1. Everyone in your class knows something about the moon. Meet in groups of four or five students each and record everything your group knows about the moon and what it does.

2. Come together as a whole group and take turns sharing your information about the moon. Have someone record all the information on the chalkboard.

3. Use the information on the chalkboard to answer the "Do You Know This About the Moon?" activity sheet.

4. If you do not have enough information to answer all the questions, save the activity sheet to use as you do Activities 6.7 through 6.9.

Teacher Information

The activity sheet is intended for motivation only and should not be used for evaluation.

With the exception of the earth, scientists know more about the moon than any other object in the solar system or the universe. Your students may be familiar with many scientific facts about the moon, yet not fully understand the basic motions of the earth and the moon and their relationships to the sun. The purpose of the following activities is to establish a concept of the relationships involved as objects move in a solar system. More detailed answers to the activity sheet may be found in your encyclopedia. Tides (Question 9) are not developed in these activities. If students can observe or experience tides in your region of the country, see your encyclopedia or library books for specific activities and information.

INTEGRATING: Language arts

SKILLS: Communicating

Answers to "Do You Know THIS About the Moon?"

1. The moon has a diameter of nearly 2,500 miles, roughly the same distance as from coast to coast on the Continental United States.

2. 238,900 miles

3. 28 days

4. Yes, once for each revolution

5. Apparent changes in shape of the moon

6. Changes in the portion of the lighted side of the moon that is visible from Earth

7. Earth rotates more rapidly than the moon revolves around it.

8. Configurations of the moon's surface—craters, volcanic flows, mountain ranges, etc.

9. Causes tides, possibly contributes to some earthquakes

10. 10 pounds. The pull of the moon's gravity is one sixth (1/6) that of the earth.

DO YOU KNOW THIS ABOUT THE MOON?

1. How large is the moon compared with the earth?

   _____

   _____

2. What is the average distance from the earth to the moon?

   _____

   _____

3. How long does it take the moon to revolve around the earth?

   _____

   _____

4. Since the moon always keeps the same side facing the earth, does it rotate on its own axis?

   _____

   _____

5. What are phases of the moon?

   _____

   _____

6. What causes phases of the moon?

   _____

   _____

7. Why is the moon often visible in the daytime?

   _____

   _____

8. What causes the "man in the moon"?

   _____

   _____

9. How does the moon's gravity affect the earth?

   _____

   _____

10. If you weigh 60 pounds on the earth, how much would you weigh on the moon?

    _____

    _____

Activity 6.7
WHAT IS THE APPEARANCE OF THE SURFACE OF THE MOON?

(Small-group, teacher-directed activity in darkened room)

Materials Needed

- One large plastic foam ball
- Magnifying glass
- Brown poster paint
- Lamp with exposed light bulb
- Meter stick (yardstick), large screwdriver, or similar dull objects

Procedure

1. In a darkened room, bring a plastic foam ball to within one meter of the light bulb. Use the magnifying glass to examine the surface of the plastic foam ball (globe). Under magnification you will notice that the surface is rough and has many dents in it. Notice that the indentations cast tiny shadows. The surface of your plastic foam ball is similar to the moon's surface except the moon has more irregularities. Scientists believe the craters or dents and mountains on the moon were caused by volcanic flows (dark color) and countless numbers of collisions with large solid objects from space, mostly *meteors*.

2. Carefully use the end of a meter stick, a large screwdriver, or a similar dull object to make several additional meteor "strikes" on the moon model. (Remember, most meteors will not come straight in but will strike from different angles.) Pour brown paint (representing lava) in some of the craters.

3. Place your plastic foam ball near the light again. Observe it from two or three meters (yards) away. Can you see why there appears to be "a man in the moon"?

Teacher Information

The friction caused by the atmosphere of our earth protects us from most small meteors, usually causing them to burn up before reaching the ground. Large meteors have struck the earth in the past and will probably do so in the future. Many scientists believe that most large species of dinosaurs were killed within a short span of time by dust caused when a large meteor strike blocked the sun for several months (or years) and killed most of the vegetation upon which the dinosaurs depended for food.

Many scientists believe that the moon once had a hot liquid core but as it cooled, volcanic activity ceased and molten materials no longer flowed on the surface. Plate tectonics also ceased, and the moon's surface has become increasingly scarred by meteor damage (estimated time: 3 to 4 1/2 billion years; very heavy meteor bombardment in early years, followed by massive dark lava flows before cooling).

SKILLS: Communicating, using space-time relationships, formulating hypotheses

Activity 6.8
HOW DOES THE MOON GIVE OFF LIGHT?

Materials Needed

- Globe of earth
- White baseball-sized ball
- Flashlight

Procedure

1. Use a large globe of the earth.
2. Darken the room.
3. Hold the ball approximately 50 cm (20 in.) above and behind the globe.
4. Shine a flashlight on the globe and ball.
5. Can you find reflected "moonlight" on the dark side of the globe?
6. What can you say about this?

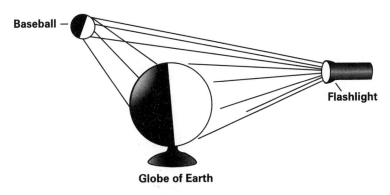

Globe, Ball, and Flashlight

Teacher Information

Some light will strike the ball and be reflected onto the dark side of the globe. This is a way of introducing the idea of night and day and moonlight. If the white ball is about one fourth the diameter of the globe, they will be in approximately the correct size ratio to each other.

The earth is visible from distances in space for the same reason the moon is visible from Earth—the sun's light reflects from its surface. If you were on the moon you would see the earth go through phases just as we see the moon go through phases, and for the same reason. And on a "full Earth" night, you would find the moon's surface to be somewhat lighted by "Earthlight," just as we experience moonlight during a full moon. Perhaps you have noticed that sometimes during a crescent moon phase, a faint outline of the rest of the moon can be seen. This is because of Earthlight.

Activity 6.9
HOW DOES THE MOON TRAVEL AROUND THE EARTH?

(Total-group activity)

 Take home and do with family and friends.

Materials Needed

- Globe of the earth
- Large plastic foam ball with "Seen from Earth" written on one side
- Round toothpick
- Small piece of gummed paper

Procedure

1. Locate on the globe the place where you live and put a tiny piece of gummed paper on that spot.
2. The foam ball represents our moon. The moon revolves around the earth once in approximately 28 days. The same side of the moon (in this case the labeled side) always faces the earth. Have another student hold the moon and walk slowly around the earth (globe) while keeping the labeled side facing the earth.
3. Rotate the globe 28 times while the moon goes around it once.
4. As the moon goes around the earth, pretend you are standing on the tiny piece of paper. Notice that part of the time you would not be able to see the moon.
5. From the model, you can easily see that you and the earth rotate and that the moon revolves. Does the moon also rotate? How can you tell?

Teacher Information

The moon rotates once each time it revolves (its period of rotation equals its period of revolution), thereby always keeping the same side facing the earth. When the model of the moon is held by a toothpick at its axis, it must be manually rotated to keep the same side facing the earth.

To give some idea of scale, the ideal-sized plastic foam ball would have approximately one fourth the diameter of the earth globe (scale size is not essential to this activity).

INTEGRATING: Language arts

SKILLS: Observing, inferring communicating, using space-time relationships, formulating hypotheses

Activity 6.10
WHAT IS A SOLAR SYSTEM?

Materials Needed

- One copy of the figure on page 122 for each student
- Paper
- Pencil

Procedure

1. Look at the drawing. This is a picture of our sun and some of the objects that move around it. The strong gravitational attraction of the sun and the weaker pull of the smaller objects keep them in orbit around the sun.

2. Count the planets shown in the diagram. Scientists have identified nine planets and a ring of millions of solid particles called the asteroid belt.

3. On your paper write the names of the four planets closest to the sun. These are sometimes called the rocky planets because they are made of solid materials. The earth is a rocky planet.

4. Write the names of the next two planets. These are sometimes called the giant planets. They are very large and in many ways like the sun.

5. Write the names of the last three planets. These are often called the icy planets because they are so far from the sun their temperatures are very, very cold. Some scientists believe there are other planets even farther out in the solar system. Perhaps, as you are reading this material, another planet may be discovered!

Teacher Information

The diagram of the solar system is not presented in scale. Because of the immense contrast in size and distance, Activities 6.12 and 6.13 suggest some ways to portray these differences.

As is shown in the diagram, the orbits of most planets are on a similar plane in relation to the sun. The orbit of Pluto is at a different angle. Scientists have several theories to account for this phenomenon. Your encyclopedia is a good reference source if students are interested.

No attempt has been made to mention or name the many moons or rings in orbit around the planets. Within the past few years, the number of planets known to have rings and the number of known moons has increased. Journals, such as the *National Geographic*, are excellent sources for current information.

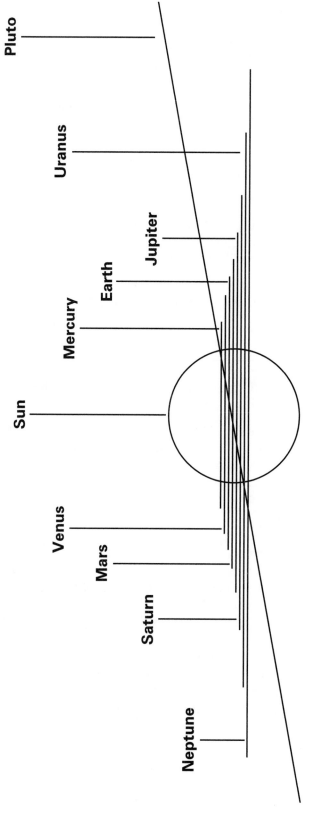

The Solar System

Activity 6.11
HOW CAN YOU STUDY A PLANET?

(Groups of five or six students)

Materials Needed

- Library books, magazines, encyclopedias, newspaper articles
- Pencil
- Paper

Procedure

1. The information we read about our solar system and other bodies in the sky is increasing rapidly. Choose a planet you would like to study and join other students to form a group.

2. Use the books and other reference materials to find out as much as you can about your planet. The following may help you begin your study:

   a. Where did your planet get its name?

   b. How was it discovered?

   c. How big is it?

   d. How far is it from the sun?

   e. How long is a day on your planet? How long is a year?

   f. What is the average temperature on your planet?

   g. Do you think you could live on your planet? Why or why not?

   h. Pretend you are on a spaceship flying near your planet. Draw a picture of what you see.

   i. Tell why your planet is unique and not like any others.

3. Plan a way to share your findings with the rest of the class.

Teacher Information

The earth should not be included in the planets studied. Knowledge of the earth will increase, since it is used as a base or standard with which other planets are compared. Not all planets need to be studied in depth.

Major goals of the activity will be met if students gain some idea of the vast differences found among the planets and the growing and changing nature of the information we have about them. It is not recommended that students be required to memorize factual information about the solar system or the universe. Very general concepts that lead to some understanding of the awesome nature of the universe should be the goal. Remember, if you were one of the unfortunate persons forced to memorize facts about astronomy, much of what you learned is now hopelessly out of date. Current issues of science journals and the *National Geographic* are excellent sources of current information on the known planets.

INTEGRATING: Reading, language arts

SKILLS: Communicating, comparing and contrasting, researching

Activity 6.12
HOW BIG IS THE SOLAR SYSTEM?

(Group activity)

Materials Needed

- Ping-Pong ball
- Two grains of sand

Procedure

1. The pictures and diagrams you have been using do not show the real sizes and distances in the solar system. It is difficult to construct a scale model that will fit in your class-room. First, pretend the Ping-Pong ball is the sun. Compare it with a grain of sand. If you pretend the grain of sand is the earth, the earth and sun are in approximate scale to each other. About one million earths could fit inside the sun. More than 100 earths could be lined up bumper to bumper across the diameter of the sun.

2. Put the Ping-Pong ball in the center of the room. Measure 3 1/2 meters (almost 4 yards) from the ball and place the grain of sand at that point. The sun (represented by the Ping-Pong ball) and the earth (represented by the grain of sand) are now in approximate scale, both in size and distance.

3. Pluto in this scale model would be another grain of sand about one fourth the size of the earth, but you would not be able to see it without a very strong telescope because it would be nearly 100 meters (about 100 yards) away from the sun (Ping-Pong ball).

4. Think of a football field. It is measured in yards. The field is 100 yards long with white lines running across it at five-yard intervals. Roughly, if you put the Ping-Pong ball (sun) on one goal line, the grain of sand representing the earth would be located near the five-yard line. Pluto, the smaller grain of sand, would be located on the far goal line 100 yards away.

Teacher Information

The scale measurements used in this activity are broad estimates. The differences in size and distance are almost incomprehensible for most young people and adults. Concrete activities such as this may help to give at least a tiny glimpse of the vastness of our solar system and universe.

INTEGRATING: Math, language arts

SKILLS: Observing, inferring, measuring, communicating, comparing and contrasting, using space-time relationships, formulating hypotheses, identifying and controlling variables

Activity 6.13
HOW CAN YOU MAKE A DISTANCE SCALE SOLAR SYSTEM IN YOUR SCHOOL?

(Total-group activity)

Materials Needed

- Nine strips of oaktag 2 cm x 4 cm (1 in. x 2 in.)
- Different-sized buttons and juice, soup, and soft-drink cans
- Different-colored paper (not black)
- Meter stick or yardstick
- Black marking pen
- Masking tape
- Ball of heavy string
- Long hallway (or auditorium)
- Yellow circle with 30 cm (12 in.) diameter

Procedure

1. Tape the yellow circle to one end of the hall (or auditorium). Label it "Sun." In this model, the *sizes* of the sun and planets will not be in scale.

2. Use different-sized buttons as patterns to draw circles on colored paper to represent the smaller planets, Mercury, Venus, Earth, Mars, and Pluto.

3. Use cans of different sizes as patterns for Jupiter, Saturn, Uranus, and Neptune. Remember Jupiter and Saturn are *much* larger than the others.

4. Write the name of a planet on each of the nine strips of oak tag.

5. Tape the planet and its name in order from the sun along the wall of the hall (or auditorium) of your school. Use your meter stick to measure the following distances from the sun:

   a. Mercury   39   centimeters
   b. Venus   72   centimeters
   c. Earth   1.00   meter
   d. Mars   1.52   meters
   e. Jupiter   5.20   meters
   f. Saturn   9.52   meters
   g. Uranus   19.60   meters
   h. Neptune   29.99   meters
   i. Pluto   39.37   meters

The distances were computed by using a measure called an *astronomical unit* (AU). The distance from the earth to the sun, 149,600,000 kilometers (93,000,000 miles), is one AU. The distance of one meter has been assigned to each AU.

6. Your planets are now in rough-scale distance from the sun. Close your eyes and try to imagine how far they really are in space.

Teacher Information

If you use pictures of the planets drawn by the students, steps 2 and 3 should be omitted. The scales and distances used in Activities 6.12 and 6.13 are only rough estimates intended to give a feeling of comparative size and distance.

If you do not have a long hallway or auditorium, go outdoors and measure and tape the planets to a long piece of string.

INTEGRATING: Math, language arts

SKILLS: Observing, inferring, measuring, communicating, using space-time relationships, formulating hypotheses, identifying and controlling variables

Activity 6.14
HOW CAN WE LEARN MORE ABOUT THE SOLAR SYSTEM AND SPACE?

(Enrichment activity)

Materials Needed

- Library books, magazines, newspaper articles, and encyclopedias
- Filmstrips, recordings, and photos
- Drawing paper and lined paper
- Paints, crayons, and other art supplies and media
- Videos of recent space explorations

Procedure

In your classroom there are books, magazines, newspaper articles, and other materials to help you learn more about the solar system and space. Find out as much as you can about one or more of the following questions and prepare a report for the class:

1. What are comets?
2. What are meteors?
3. Do meteors ever strike the earth?
4. What causes meteor showers?
5. How big is the planet Jupiter?
6. How does Jupiter affect other objects in the solar system (both now and in the past)?
7. If you had to try to live on another planet or moon in the solar system, which would you choose, and why?
8. If you wanted to become an astronaut, when, how, and where would you begin?
9. Some animals such as coyotes and wolves are known to howl during a full moon. See if you can find stories or legends about ways the full moon is thought to affect people.
10. Choose a special interest of your own, not listed above, and make a study of it.

Teacher Information

Major areas of importance not developed in this section include the effect of tides on water, land, and atmosphere, the profound effect of Jupiter's strong gravitational field, the effect of variations in the sun's atmosphere, theories as to the origin of the solar system and universe, and the probability of the existence of other solar systems—with a real possibility of some form of life beyond the earth. These topics may suggest other areas of study or discussion for motivated students.

INTEGRATING: Reading, language arts

SKILLS: Communicating, using space-time relationships, formulating hypotheses, researching

LIFE SCIENCE ACTIVITIES

Topics

- **Plants and Seeds**
- **Animals**
- **Growing and Changing: Animal Life Cycles**
- **Animal Adaptations**
- **Body Systems**
- **The Five Senses**
- **Health and Nutrition**

Topic 7: Plants and Seeds

TO THE TEACHER

A study of plants affords many opportunities for creative imagination. Throughout the study, appreciation of beauty and the wonder of growth should be emphasized. Language arts, music, art, and other subjects should be related as often as possible.

Teachers in urban areas may find some difficulty in conducting a few of the field trip activities; however, window boxes and artificial growing areas may be substituted.

Resource people can be valuable in this area. Most classrooms have mothers or fathers who grow plants as a hobby. Agronomists (soil specialists), horticulturists, florists, botanists, and nutritionists can also be helpful in their areas of specialization. Designing and planting a school garden could be a very worthwhile outgrowth of this study.

Throughout the study, care should be taken to emphasize the danger of eating any unknown substance. Even some parts of plants we eat can be poisonous, such as rhubarb leaves and some varieties of potato plant leaves. Warn children never to eat berries or flowers. On field trips, take into account regional variations to avoid such things as poison ivy and stinging nettle.

Most growing activities suggest the use of potting soil; however, as plants develop they will usually do better in rich, loamy soil. Specialized plants such as cactuses and pine trees will need special alkali or acid soils. Be sure to check reference sources before growing specialized plants.

Older children may be interested in solving a problem as a plant scientist might. Several plants in the same kinds of containers could be presented with the following statement and question:

These are all the same species of plant, planted on the same day from similar seeds. How can you account for the differences?

The plants used will have been grown in different media—gravel, sand, potting soil, or loam. One will have been put in a dark place, one in sunlight. One will have been overwatered, one underwatered. As children observe differences in the conditions of the plants, soil, and moisture, they will form hypotheses they can test through replication: identifying a problem (Some plants don't grow as well as others); stating a hypothesis (This plant is too dry); testing the hypothesis (If I transplant this plant to soil instead of gravel it will grow better); conclusion (What I tried worked or didn't work). This activity is similar to the work of agricultural specialists.

Activity 7.1
CAN WE COMMUNICATE WITH PLANTS?

(This is a "just-for-fun" activity)

Materials Needed

- Six to eight house plants of the same variety, age, and vigor
- Sensitive scale to weigh grams and ounces (food scale)
- 9″ × 12″ newsprint
- Markers
- Player and records or tapes of different kinds of music
- Name tags

Information

Scientists have long wondered if there might be a way to communicate with plants. Although there has never been any scientific evidence that plants can talk or hear, you may be communicating with them in special ways through the care you give them. Most plants need sunlight, water, warmth, and the correct kind of soil. Do they need anything else? Just for fun, try some of these things. As you begin, you will probably think of many more ideas to try.

Procedure

1. Make pictures and describe each plant. Measure them and weigh them. Record all measurements.

2. Name all but one of your plants and attach the names to their containers. When you come near them to water or move them always use their names and ask them how they are feeling. Care for the plant without a name in exactly the same way but don't talk to it.

3. Put two of your plants with names closer together. Isolate the plant without a name.

4. Play soft, soothing music to two of your plants daily, for one hour. Play loud harsh music to two others.

5. Try other ideas on different plants, but remember to do just one thing different to any plant. Keep a record of what you did to each plant. Be sure all plants are adequately watered.

6. After two or three weeks, bring all your plants together. Observe them. Make pictures of them. Weigh them and measure them again. What can you say abut this experience?

7. Remember, this is not a scientific experiment. *It's just for fun.*

Teacher Information

Although there is no scientific evidence that plants communicate with humans or each other in a linguistic sense, there is some evidence to suggest that certain varieties of plants (trees) may send out a message to others of the same variety when they are under attack by insects or fungus.

People who love plants may ascribe personalities to them, talk to them, and give them better care, on which they will thrive. This could lead to an interesting discussion of how plants should be treated in our society.

Activity 7.2
HOW CAN WE MAKE A VISUAL RECORD OF PLANT GROWTH?

Materials Needed

- A newly started plant
- Chart paper
- Colored construction paper
- Scissors
- Ruler
- Tape or glue

Procedure

1. Write "Days of Measured Growth" at the bottom of the chart paper.
2. Write "Height in centimeters" (or "inches" if you prefer) up the left side of the chart paper.
3. Measure the height of your plant, from the soil to the tip of the plant.
4. Cut a narrow strip of colored construction paper the same length as the plant's height.
5. Tape or glue the strip of colored paper to the chart paper, positioned vertically near the lower left (see the following illustration).
6. Write "1" on the chart paper below the strip of paper, indicating that this strip shows how tall the plant was on the first day it was measured.
7. Measure the height of the plant every other day. For each measure, cut another strip of paper the appropriate length (height of the plant), mount the paper to the chart, and write the number of the day at the bottom, counting days from the day of the first measurement.
8. Does your plant grow faster as it gets older? Does it slow down? Do you notice a change when you forget to water it?
9. Discuss the growth pattern of your plant with your group. Compare the growth pattern with that of other plants included in this study.

For Problem Solvers: Set up an experiment to determine the effect of light on plant growth. This is a good time to invite one or more others to work with you, if you want to do that. After you write up your plan, discuss it with your teacher. Be sure you use a control.

Use the technique you learned in this activity to track the growth of each plant. Identify at the top of the chart the experiment (such as "Effect of Light on Plant Growth") and which plant(s) is being recorded on this chart.

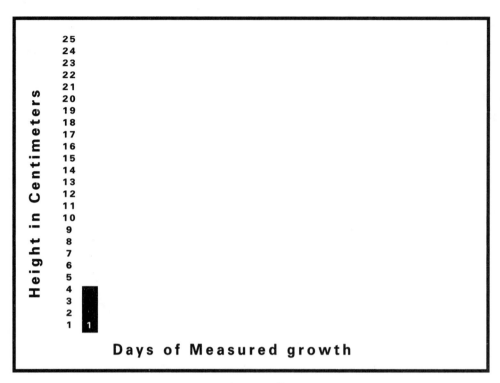

Height in Centimeters

25
24
23
22
21
20
19
18
17
16
15
14
13
12
11
10
9
8
7
6
5
4
3
2
1

1

Days of Measured growth

Plant Growth Chart

Teacher Information

In this activity students will use a vertical bar graph to keep a record of the growth of one or more plants. This skill will be useful in future work with plants and in many other applications.

Your problem solvers, who wish to extend their study of plants, can use this method of charting the growth of plants they use as they investigate the effect of light on plant growth. You might suggest that they also consider investigating the effect of varying moisture conditions, amounts and types of fertilizer, soil types, age of seed, or any other variable related to plant growth.

INTEGRATING: Math, art

SKILLS: Observing, inferring, measuring, predicting, communicating, comparing and contrasting, using space-time relationships, formulating hypotheses, identifying and controlling variables, experimenting

Activity 7.3
WHY ARE LEAVES IMPORTANT?

Materials Needed

- Variety of plants—perhaps some you gather on a nearby field trip
- Pictures of plants similar to your plants
- Paper towel
- Book

Procedure

1. Spread your plants out flat on your desk.
2. Study them carefully and compare their roots, stems, and leaves.
3. In what ways are they alike? In what ways are they different? Can you think of reasons why?

Leaf

4. Choose some of your most interesting leaves and spread them out on a piece of paper towel. Put another paper towel on top of them, then place a flat, heavy object, such as a book, on top. This is called pressing. Wait several days and remove the weight. If you would care to preserve your leaves, ask your teacher for help.
5. Leaves are very important to plants and to many other forms of life on earth. Do you know why? Discuss your ideas with others.

For Problem Solvers: Do some research about leaves. Your encyclopedia will have some very interesting information. See what you can find out about the importance of leaves to the plant. Why are they important to animals? Do you ever eat leaves? What are some of the largest and smallest leaves? Why do many leaves change colors in the autumn? How many different shapes of leaves can you find? Classify your leaves by putting them into groups that seem logical to you. How many different ways can you find that people use leaves?

Share your information with your group.

Teacher Information

The shape, color, and texture of leaves can be an interesting study. Pressing, preserving, and displaying leaves in creative ways may add aesthetic dimensions to the activity. An excellent way to preserve leaves is to laminate them. They may also be preserved by pressing them with a warm iron between sheets of waxed paper. Leaves are important to plants because they manufacture food through their "chlorophyll factories." Plants also "breathe" through their leaves. In the daytime (during photosynthesis) they give off oxygen. In darkness their chlorophyll factories shut down. For additional information about leaves, see your encyclopedia.

INTEGRATING: Social studies, art

SKILLS: Observing, classifying, measuring, communicating, researching

Activity 7.4
HOW CAN YOU PRESERVE THE LEAVES YOU COLLECT?

 Take home and do with family and friends.

Materials Needed

- Large poster paper or cardstock
- Leaves to preserve
- Wide transparent tape

Procedure

1. Lay a leaf on the cardstock.
2. Place a strip of tape over the leaf full length, to completely seal it to the paper.
3. Place more tape over the leaf until the leaf is completely covered.
4. Get together with others who are preserving leaves. Compare your leaves with theirs and see how many different kinds you have altogether.
5. How many basic shapes can you find among the leaves? Do they have smooth edges, or are they jagged? Put your leaves into groups according to their shape.

For Problem Solvers: Small flowering plants can also be preserved in this way. Collect several small plants and preserve them by mounting them to cardstock with wide transparent tape. Press the plants flat on paper before mounting them, but you don't have to wait until they dry thoroughly.

If you want to be able to remember what type of plant each one in the collection is, find this information before you mount the plants to the cardstock and write the names at the bottom of the cards before mounting the plants. A permanent marker would do a nice job with the names.

Teacher Information

This type of mounting will give the plants a fair degree of permanence, without equipment or very much expense. The plants will dry slowly through the back of the cardstock but they will not be crumbly when mounted.

INTEGRATING: Reading

SKILLS: Observing, inferring, predicting, communicating, using space-time relationships, formulating hypotheses, identifying and controlling variables, experimenting, researching

Activity 7.5
HOW DO ROOTS GROW AND DEVELOP?

Materials Needed

- Several young plants that are sprouting in potting soil (same variety)
- Hand lenses

Procedure

1. Pull up one sprouting plant from the potting soil and examine the roots with a hand lens. Make a drawing of the plant, including its roots.

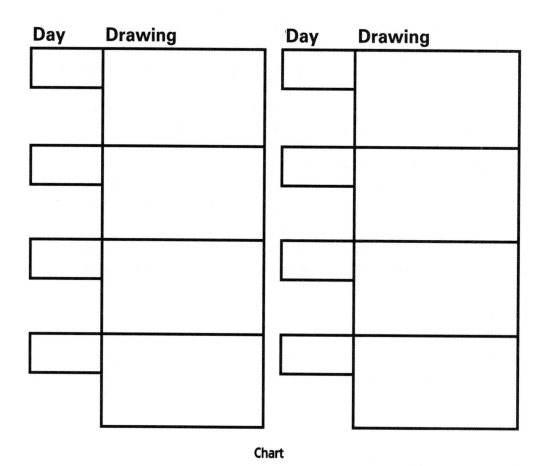

Chart

2. Pull up a different plant every other day for a week and examine its roots. Make a drawing of the plant, including roots, each time. How tall is the plant? How long are the roots?

3. Discuss the progress of the root system of these plants. What changes do you see?

For Problem Solvers: Continue your study of root structures by comparing root systems of other types of plants. Do they all have the same basic parts? Measure their growth on a weekly (or even daily) basis. How do the root structures of the different varieties of plants compare? Which ones grow faster? Slower? Which ones have the largest and most massive root structure? Which ones do you think are better designed to support a large, heavy plant in a windstorm?

Teacher Information

The plants will likely be more advanced each day, and their root systems will be more highly developed. Small hairlike roots will be growing through the soil. This activity could be continued for several weeks or could lead to a study of other plants and their root systems—especially for your problem solvers, who are motivated to continue their study.

INTEGRATING: Math, art

SKILLS: Observing, inferring, measuring, communicating, comparing and contrasting, using space-time relationships

Activity 7.6
WHAT ARE THE PARTS OF A FLOWER?

Materials Needed

- Large flowers
- Wide transparent tape
- Hand lenses
- White paper
- Roll of plastic wrap

Procedure

1. Put your flower on a sheet of white paper and examine it carefully.
2. Compare your flower with the one in the picture. Can you find the same parts? You may need a hand lens to help you.
3. Carefully take your flower apart. First find the petals, then the sepals, and then the pistil. Next find the stamens and the anther.
4. Use transparent tape to tape the parts to your sheet of white paper.
5. Label the parts, cover your paper with plastic wrap, and hang it on a wall of your classroom.

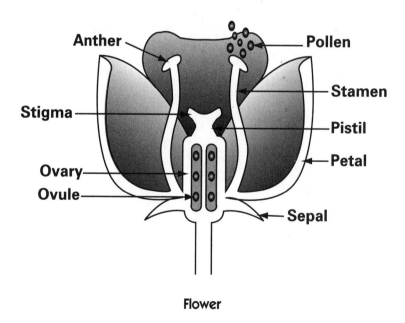

Flower

For Problem Solvers: When you are finished with your flower, try to think of a way to use the parts of it to make a collage or other kind of art project. Perhaps you can share with others, in order to have a greater variety of colors and parts.

Do some research and find out why each part of a flower is important. What is the purpose of the anther, the stamen, the ovary, and each of the other parts? Which parts are responsible for making new flowers? Where do the seeds grow? What has to happen in order for seeds to form? You will find some fascinating information. Share what you learn with your group, and with others.

How many petals does your flower have? Do all flowers have the same number of petals? Do all flowers of this type have the same number?

See how many different ways you can think of or find that people use flowers. Make a list of these and compare your list with the lists of others who do the same activity.

Teacher Information

Typical flowers have four sets of parts: sepals, petals, stamens, and the pistil, which includes the ovary and the stigma. Pollen comes from the top of the stamens, which are supported by thin filaments. When the ovary ripens, the top of the pistil, called the stigma, will become sticky and collect pollen spread in the air or by insects. When a flower has all four parts it is said to be complete. Flowers lacking any of the four parts are generally classified as incomplete.

This is an excellent individual or small-group activity. Extension and enrichment activities could include collecting flowers and pictures for bulletin boards and studying flower arranging. This activity could motivate children to learn the purpose and function of flowers in nature. Flowers should be appreciated for their beauty. Memorizing the names of flower parts is of little value in the elementary school, but careful observation and firsthand experience will increase children's awareness of plants and enhance appreciation for their beauty.

INTEGRATING: Reading, math, art

SKILLS: Observing, inferring, classifying, measuring, communicating, researching

Activity 7.7
HOW CAN YOU MAKE A "DANDY" TASTING SALAD?

(Teacher-supervised activity)

Materials Needed

- Young dandelion leaves, gathered in early spring before they blossom
- Salt water
- Salt
- Pepper
- Chives
- Salad dressing
- Margarine
- Eating utensils and plates
- Plastic bag
- Heat source
- Saucepan

Procedure

1. Gather a plastic bag full of young dandelion leaves to bring to class.
2. Pull the young plants up, being careful to get as much of the root as possible.
3. Pull the leaves from the root. Rinse the leaves and boil them in salt water for about 10 minutes. Season the cooked leaves with salt and pepper and a pat of margarine. Eat your special vegetable.
4. The crowns (tops) of the roots may also be prepared in the same way to provide another variety of vegetable.
5. Mix young dandelion leaves with lettuce and celery leaves at about the ratio of one dandelion leaf to two lettuce and celery leaves. Add chives and mix thoroughly.
6. Use salad dressing to taste.
7. You now have a new special inexpensive salad to show at home.

For Problem Solvers: Some of the early settlers had to rely quite a lot on native plants for their food. Find out what plants that grow wild in your area are edible—plants that you don't normally eat. Try eating one or more of these, but be sure it's safe before eating it.

Also try to find out where potatoes, corn, and other common food crops began. How did people first learn about them as a food source? Have these plants been altered over the years to make them more desirable? How does that happen?

144

Teacher Information

Dandelions (*Thraxacum officinale*) must be picked while they are very young. Boiling in salt water will help remove the bitter taste. **CAUTION: Be sure the leaves are not gathered in areas that have been sprayed.** The bulbs of roots may be treated the same as leaves. Even young dandelion leaves may be somewhat bitter. In using them in fresh salad, be sure to use plenty of lettuce. This may be an appropriate time to remind children not to eat unknown leaves or other parts of plants, such as berries or flowers. Dandelion leaves are a source of vitamins A and C.

INTEGRATING: Social studies

SKILLS: Observing, classifying, communicating, using space-time relationships, formulating hypotheses, researching

Activity 7.8
WHAT HAVE WE LEARNED?

(Teacher-supervised activity)

Materials Needed

- Assorted fresh fruits
- Vegetables
- Nuts
- Juices
- Salad greens
- Sprouts
- Bread or rolls and margarine from previous activity
- Paper plates
- Cooking utensils
- Bowls
- Plastic knives, forks, spoons
- Seasoning
- Salt
- Pepper
- Napkins
- Stove or hot plate

Procedure

1. Use the list of plant foods to plan a luncheon meal.
2. Make a menu describing the items you will prepare and serve. Try to use as many adjectives as you can to make everyone want to try all the foods you prepare.
3. Have your teacher help cut and cook your meal.
4. Invite special people to have lunch with you. Don't forget the school cook or cafeteria workers.

For Problem Solvers: Learn to bake bread or prepare one or more other specific foods at home. Ask your teacher if you could bring samples to class for the other students to try. Experiment with one or more of the ingredients to try to improve the dish or at least to find out what effect that particular ingredient has on the texture, taste, etc. Before you actually use the altered recipe, write the change you will make and the effect you expect it to have on the finished product.

Teacher Information

This activity combined with the dandelion salad activity can be an enjoyable culmination to this study. In addition to preparing and serving food, students may choose to share reports, pictures, songs, and other information acquired during the study. Planning and writing the menu, designing invitations, giving reports, sharing art work, singing songs, decorating the room with plants and flowers they have grown, and learning how to be good hosts and hostesses should be a planned part of this activity.

Note: You will need to plan well in advance to arrange for parents and aides to assist with the preparation and cooking. A prior activity on bread making could be developed (good place for a mother or father to be asked to help).

INTEGRATING: Reading, math, language arts, social studies

SKILLS: Observing, inferring, measuring, predicting, communicating, formulating hypotheses, identifying and controlling variables, experimenting

Activity 7.9
IS THIS A PLANT?

Materials Needed

- Bread, jelly, orange, cheese, and other foods
- Hand lenses
- Plastic margarine containers and lids

Procedure

1. Choose four different foods and place each one in a container. Put the lids on and place each container in a warm, dark place. (If you choose bread, be sure it is moist.)
2. In four or five days remove the lid of each container and observe the contents.
3. What has happened to the food?

Teacher Information

With the most recently adopted classification system, mold is no longer classified as a plant. This activity will introduce mold in a controlled environment. Most children have seen mold, but only in the context of something that has "spoiled" or been ruined. The following activities will help children learn more about mold and how it is both harmful and helpful in their lives. The containers used in these activities should be clean and thoroughly rinsed. Soap residue may retard the growth of mold.

Most activities are excellent individual or small-group activities. Teacher demonstration and classroom discussion should come only after each child has had firsthand experience with the activities.

SKILLS: Observing, inferring, communicating, using space-time relationships, formulating hypotheses

Activity 7.10
WHAT IS THIS STRANGE GROWTH?

Materials Needed

- Containers and foods used in Activity 7.9
- Hand lenses
- Drawing paper
- Markers

Procedure

1. Examine the contents of each of your containers.
2. Use a hand lens to study the growths on the food in each container.
3. Draw a picture of what you observe. Use as much detail as you can.
4. Touch your strange organism. Wash your hands after you touch it. Sniff it without getting too close. Do you notice an odor?
5. Under your picture, write some words to tell what you saw, felt, and smelled.
6. Be prepared to bring your containers and picture to share with the rest of the class.
7. Also be prepared with questions to ask your teacher.

Teacher Information

Your media center or school library may have children's books about mold. Children should be encouraged to use the books, but not before they have completed the activities. Elementary and junior high school books are excellent sources for teacher background information and pupil reference for older children. It is recommended that reports be encouraged but not required.

CAUTION: After children touch the mold, remind them to wash their hands thoroughly before touching anything else, especially their eyes. Children with bronchial problems should be cautioned not to get close to the mold or sniff it. This might be an opportunity to discuss the dangers of tasting, smelling, or touching unfamiliar materials.

SKILLS: Observing, inferring, communicating, formulating hypotheses, researching

Activity 7.11
WHAT DOES YOUR STRANGE ORGANISM GROW ON?

Materials Needed

- Miscellaneous living (or once-living) and nonliving things, such as cut-up fruit, melons, potato, cheese, bread, wool, nails, magnets, rocks, and wood
- Plastic margarine containers and lids

Procedure

1. Choose five different items from the table.

2. Put each item in a plastic container with the top sealed.

3. On which items do you think the strange plants will grow? On which do you think they won't? Be prepared to explain your reasons.

4. Place your containers in a warm, dark place.

5. After five or six days open your containers and observe the results.

6. Compare your observations with the ideas you had about which would and which would not grow. Were your ideas correct? Can you think of reasons why?

For Problem Solvers: Select one material, such as bread, and repeat the activity, changing one variable. For example, place dry bread in a warm, dark place and compare it with moist bread for the same length of time in a warm, dark place. Do you think dry bread will support the growth of mold as well as moist bread? You might also try a freezer, which provides a cold and dark environment.

What other variables will you try with this experiment? Remember to change only one variable at a time.

Share your findings with your group and compare what you learned with what others who did this activity learned.

Teacher Information

This activity is designed to help students see relationships, to reason, and to hypothesize. It has been used most successfully with students well into the concrete operational years, grades four through eight. The most obvious conclusion should be that mold grows on living (or once-living) things and not on inorganic material. Molds use the once-living materials for food. Given enough time and proper conditions, mold will cause wood to rot, but probably not within the time allowed for this activity.

INTEGRATING: Reading, math

SKILLS: Observing, inferring, classifying, measuring, predicting, communicating, using space-time relationships, formulating hypotheses, identifying and controlling variables, experimenting, researching

Activity 7.12
WHAT HAVE WE LEARNED ABOUT MOLD?

(Total-group activity)

Materials Needed

- Containers of mold from previous activities
- Student drawings
- Books and pictures from media center, public library, and home

Procedure

1. Participate in a class discussion about mold. Share and compare your findings from Activities 7.10 and 7.11 with those of the other students.
2. Ask any questions you may have.
3. Use your pictures and containers to design a display and bulletin board about mold.

For Problem Solvers: Are molds harmful, or are they helpful? Think carefully before you answer that question. Discuss the question with your group. Consider what would be different without molds and other organisms that break down organic material.

Make a list of ways that molds can be helpful and ways they can be harmful.

Teacher Information

After studies about mold, consider preparing an informational audiotape to be used after a class discussion. The tape may help answer questions or reinforce concepts identified during the discussion. Try to help children *discover* the answers through sharing and studying reference sources. Avoid telling them more than is necessary. The following are concepts you may want to include on the audiotape or in your summary:

1. Most molds look somewhat like cotton. Many are not white, but they have a "cottony" texture.
2. Molds grow best in warm, damp, dark places. Mold is a problem in parts of the United States where the climate is humid and warm.
3. Mold often damages food, leather, clothing, and paper. Some molds cause diseases in man, plants, food crops, and animals.
4. Many molds are helpful. They cause wood, leaves, and other materials to rot, forming humus, which makes the soil rich. People use mold to make drugs, such as penicillin. Molds also produce carbon dioxide, which green plants use to make food. Mold is deliberately allowed to grow on Roquefort and certain other types of cheese to help ripen it.
5. Mold reproduces by releasing spores, which travel through the air or are carried by animals.

INTEGRATING: Reading, language arts, social studies

SKILLS: Classifying, communicating

Topic 8: Animals

TO THE TEACHER

The study of animals is so broad that it can, and often does, encompass a lifetime. In this section we have tried to limit our study to some of the animals in our immediate environment. We have focused on the following general areas:

- Pets and Imaginary Animals
- Relatives of Pets (Animal Tracks)
- Animals in Our Neighborhood (Nature Square)
- Animals Outside Our Window (Birds)
- Animals in Our Room (Aquariums; Terrariums)

Many broad categories such as domesticated animals, animal colonies, animals of the zoo, and exotic animals have been omitted. You are encouraged to study these areas, using the skills and resources developed in the following activities.

This section places a strong emphasis on the use of books, other media, and resource persons. Before you begin, read through the materials lists so you can begin organizing, collecting, and arranging for future activities.

The nature square requires outside activities and field trips.

There are also several simple construction projects such as bird feeders, birdhouses, and butterfly nets. Enlist the help of parents and others.

To complete some activities, small costs may be involved. Inexpensive hand lenses, animals, and plants may need to be purchased. In some cases, orders may have to be sent to science supply houses, and delivery time will be a factor.

We urge you to use resource people whenever possible. There are amateur as well as professional naturalists everywhere.

The main purpose of these activities is to help students develop respect and appreciation for the variety, beauty, and wonder of the animals around them.

Be as creative as you can. Wander and explore in any direction you choose. These activities could be starting points for lifelong interests and hobbies.

All of the following activities can be adapted for use with young children. Occasionally, specific suggestions for adaptation are made, but usually we have attempted to present ideas that are flexible enough to be used with any age group.

Perhaps to prepare yourself for this adventure you could read Robert Frost's poem, "The Vantage Point." You can find a vantage point wherever you are.

Activity 8.1
WHAT CLUES CAN HELP US READ TRACKS?

Materials Needed

- Drawings of common animal tracks of dog, cat, squirrel, deer (numbered but unnamed)
- Paper
- Crayons

Procedure

1. Study the animal tracks in the picture. You have probably seen one or two of these tracks before in dust, dirt, sand, or snow.

2. Compare the tracks. How many toes can you count on each? Which have claws? Can you tell how many have foot pads? What is different about track 4?

3. The tracks belong to the following animals: squirrel, dog, cat, and deer. Think of each animal. On your paper write those four animal names and write the number of the track above the name of each animal.

4. Compare your answers with others in the class.

5. Animals that belong to the same family make similar tracks. If you changed the size and the shape slightly you could rename the tracks: mountain lion, wolf, elk, chipmunk. Match these four animals with the animals and tracks that you already have on your paper.

6. Compare your animal pairs with those of others in your group. Ask your teacher for the correct information.

1   2   3   4

Comparing Four Animal Tracks

For Problem Solvers: Using the encyclopedia and other books that you have available, along with your own experience, add at least one animal to each of the four groups that match the animal tracks used in this activity.

Select another type of animal, draw its track, and make a list of the animals you think would make that shape of track. Share your work with others in your group, check each other's work, and learn from each other.

Why was it important for the early settlers to recognize the tracks of wild animals? Discuss this question with your group.

Teacher Information

The drawings in the figure are tracks of a dog (1), cat (2), squirrel (3), and deer (4).

Other members of the same family whose tracks are similar are:

Dog	Cat	Squirrel	Deer
Wolf	Mountain Lion	Chipmunk	Elk
Coyote	Bobcat	Groundhog	Moose

The purpose of this activity is to help children understand that although animal tracks are different, members of the same families make similar-shaped tracks. Thus the track of a dog accompanying a hunter may make a track similar to that of a wolf or a coyote. There may be several varieties of squirrels and chipmunks in the park whose tracks look alike. Tracks give only one clue to the identification and behavior of animals.

For cats, many students will probably choose a track with claws because of the association of cats with being scratched. Members of the cat family, with one exception, have retractable claws that are usually drawn into a sheath when they walk and extended when they climb, attack, or defend. The cheetah, the fastest runner on Earth for short distances, is the only cat that does not have retractable claws.

INTEGRATING: Reading, language arts, social studies, art

SKILLS: Observing, inferring, classifying, communicating, comparing and contrasting, researching

Activity 8.2
WHAT DO YOU NEED IN ORDER TO STUDY A NATURE SQUARE?

Materials Needed

- Meter stick or string 10 meters (10 yards) long
- Wooden stakes or markers to show borders
- "Observation Chart for Nature Square" (see the following illustration)
- 9" × 12" heavy white paper (for mapping)
- Crayons

Procedure

1. Study the list of materials on the Observation Chart. This is the beginning of a list of things you will be looking for when you visit the special place you have chosen, which will be called a "nature square." Notice there are extra spaces at the bottom for you to add unusual or different things you find.

2. When you first visit your square, use the string or meter stick to make approximate measures of its size. Remember, your square does not have to be a real square shape. It could be long, round, or kidney-shaped. Put wooden stakes or markers around the border.

3. On your first visit to the square, make a picture-map of the distinctive features (things that stand out) such as rocks, trees, bushes, or water areas.

4. Report your initial (first) findings to the class.

Teacher Information

In the following activities students will be expected to make periodic visits to the places they have selected. Try to help them select areas that will be inviting to as many forms of wildlife as possible.

Areas should be large enough to include many of the features mentioned in step 1 of the preceding activity, but not so large as to be unmanageable. Shape is important only if it can be altered to include special features such as a tree, pond, or shaded area.

If students or their parents have simple cameras, actual photographs could be included but should not replace the picture-map activity suggested in this activity.

Activity 8.3 gives specific instructions for using the observation chart.

INTEGRATING: Language arts, art

SKILLS: Observing, inferring, classifying, measuring, communicating

OBSERVATION CHART FOR NATURE SQUARE				
Date of visit				
General conditions: climate, wind, temperature, precipitation, and so on				
Vegetation: trees, shrubs, weeds, flowers, grass, and so on				
Small underground animals: ants. worms, beetles, bugs, and so on				
Small animals on the ground and under rocks, leaves, or other ground cover: spiders, ants, and so on				
Small animals on or in vegetation: aphids, caterpillars, larvae, eggs, bugs, beetles, and so on				
Small flying insects: bees, beetles, gnats, butterflies, mosquitoes, grasshoppers, dragonflies, and so on				
Larger underground animals: gophers, chipmunks, moles, and so on				
Larger animals flying, nesting, perching, walking (tracks), or crawling				
Animals in standing water, pond, or lake: tadpoles, frogs, fish, snakes, salamanders, insects, and so on				
Other observations:				

Observations, Discoveries, and Conditions

Observation Chart for Nature Square

158

Activity 8.3
HOW CAN A CHART HELP US MAKE OBSERVATIONS?

Materials Needed

- "Observation Chart for Nature Square" (see Activity 8.2)
- Pencils

Procedure

1. This chart is designed to help you study your nature square.

2. The column on the far left suggests specific things you should watch for and record each time you visit your square.

3. The other smaller columns with boxes are places for you to record words to report each observation.

4. The bottom space is blank all the way across. Use it to record and report things you find that are special about your square.

5. With your teacher and other students, discuss the areas listed in the far left column. Leave out anything that does not apply to your own square.

6. Make visits to your square every other day. Write the date at the top of the column and use the chart as you study your square.

Teacher Information

The observation chart is general in nature and may need to be adapted to your particular location.

Discuss each category on the left and be certain students understand the examples. Add and delete items as necessary.

It may be helpful to go through an imaginary visit, step by step, to show them how to use the chart.

Activity 8.4 suggests guidelines for equipment to take along on visits to the square.

INTEGRATING: Language arts

SKILLS: Observing, inferring, classifying, measuring, communicating, using space-time relationships, researching

Activity 8.4
WHAT EQUIPMENT CAN HELP US STUDY OUR NATURE SQUARE?

Materials Needed

- Shoe boxes
- Hand lenses
- Metal spoons
- Dull table knives
- Scissors or garden shears
- Tweezers (or forceps)
- Mosquito netting
- Small-to-large jars with lids or assorted rigid plastic containers with lids
- Small cans with hinged lids
- Small-to-large plastic bags
- Butterfly nets
- Notebook and pencils
- Tape, string, and rubber bands

Procedure

1. Look at the list of materials. You can probably gather most of the equipment around your home and school.

2. Put a mark by the items you think you can find.

3. Discuss the list with your teacher and class. Perhaps you can trade with others to get the things you don't have.

4. After the class discussion make a list of things you still need and ask your teacher for help in locating them.

5. Gather the materials. Put the smaller items in a shoe box and the larger items in a plastic bag (pack glass in paper).

6. Scientists called *naturalists* study nature as you are going to do. The simple equipment you have is very similar to the equipment they use.

7. After you have gathered your equipment, you are ready to begin investigating your nature square just as a naturalist would do.

For Problem Solvers: Visit with a biologist, forest ranger, or other naturalist. Ask this person to tell you about the equipment he or she uses in studying life forms in an area in nature. Compare their equipment with your list and see how many of their items you can match with items in the list that will accomplish a similar purpose.

Share your information with your group.

Teacher Information

A simple plan for making butterfly nets is shown in the following illustration. Construction can be done by every child or they can work in groups of three or four.

Before you begin studying and collecting specimens discuss the following simple safety rules:

1. Don't put anything you find in your mouth.

2. Be very careful with insects that sting, such as bees, hornets, and wasps (never disturb their nests).

3. Use a spoon or envelope to scoop crawling insects into containers.

4. If any animals are removed from the nature square, they should have comfortable housing and later be returned alive.

5. Always wash your hands as soon as possible after visiting the nature square.

6. Attend to accidental cuts, scratches, or bites as soon as they occur.

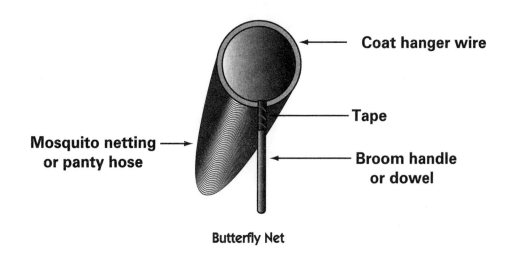

Coat hanger wire

Tape

Mosquito netting or panty hose

Broom handle or dowel

Butterfly Net

If there are poisonous plants or animals common to your region of the country, such as poison ivy, poison oak, ticks, or chiggers be sure the children can identify and avoid these specimens.

High-quality hand lenses are not necessary for field study. Lenses molded from plastic are sold in the school equipment or stationery departments of most general merchandise (variety) stores. You will, however, need several high-quality hand lenses for classroom use.

Items not included in the kit are insect-killing jars and materials to preserve and mount specimens. The focus of this section is on the observation and study of nature as it exists. If specimens are brought to school, every effort should be made to put them in a suitable container and when appropriate try to include a portion of their immediate surroundings—twigs, leaves, soil. A small, moist sponge or piece of apple, pear, or peach, and plenty of fresh air should be provided for insects. Jars with small holes punched in the top do not provide enough air circulation. Use a piece of mosquito netting held with a rubber band over the top of the container. After study, all live specimens should be released where they were collected. Caution students not to bring injured or baby birds to the classroom.

This could be an excellent opportunity to involve parents and other groups. They can help in collecting and organizing equipment.

INTEGRATING: Language arts, social studies

SKILLS: Observing, inferring, classifying, measuring, communicating, using space-time relationships, researching

Activity 8.5
HOW CAN WE REPORT OUR FINDINGS?

(Class discussion with older students)

Materials Needed

- Paper
- Pencil
- Calendar (optional)

Procedure

1. Visit your nature square about every other day for a period of two or three weeks. Use a calendar to write the specific dates you plan to go. When you sign your name to this paper and give it to your teacher it will mean that you agree to visit your square on the days listed, spend at least 30 minutes, make observations, collect specimens when possible, and keep a record on your observation chart. When your paper is accepted it will mean that your teacher agrees to assist you in your study and in the evaluation of what you have done. This then becomes a *contract*.

2. Plan with your teacher and other members of the class on how your study will be shared. Scientists hold conferences to share their ideas with each other. They often give oral reports from notes. Sometimes they meet in small, informal groups to share and compare their important discoveries. Some get together to write books, or magazine and newspaper articles. They usually find some way to communicate their important findings to others. As a group of naturalists, how will you report your findings so others will know what you have observed and discovered?

For Problem Solvers: Compare the types of plants and animals found in all areas used by the class for nature squares. In cases where there are differences in the types of plants and animals, discuss possible reasons. Analyze the nature squares in terms of location, moisture, amount of sunlight, nearness to traffic or homes, and other characteristics that might explain the differences in life forms found there.

Teacher Information

Omit step 1 if you have made the study during class time on the school grounds or a nearby vacant lot. *Contracting* is a technique some teachers have found helpful in encouraging responsibility and independent work. Parents are sometimes asked to sign a contract, too.

The length of time students spend studying their squares will vary according to the situation, but stating a specific minimum time is usually helpful.

Students may need help in developing skills of observation. Remind them to move slowly and quietly and sit for lengths of time. Shy animals will reveal themselves only if they think they are alone. Encourage children to use their senses (except taste). Listening is often as important as looking.

A study of a nature square will provide many opportunities for the use of books and other media as they are available. Handbooks and field guides for identification of insects, spiders, birds, snakes, flowers, and plants will be especially helpful.

If they are available, filmstrips or videos can be of great help in supplementing this area of study.

As you identify insects and spiders of different kinds, classify them into harmful, coexisting, and helpful categories as they relate to man. Although many people dislike them, spiders are usually harmless and are very valuable in the control of harmful insects.

Figures 8.5-1 through 8.5-3 show an insect, a spider, and a mouse. These should be helpful for quick classification so children can pursue further identification in field books.

INTEGRATING: Reading, language arts, social studies, art

SKILLS: Observing, inferring, classifying, communicating, researching

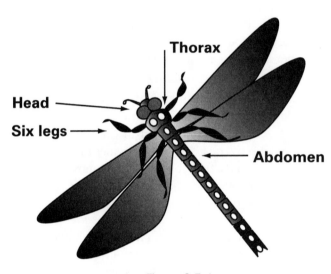

Figure 8.5-1

Dragonfly

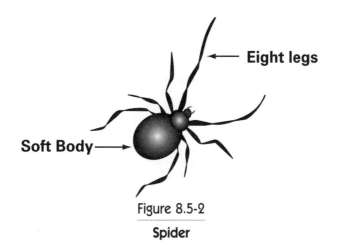

Eight legs

Soft Body

Figure 8.5-2

Spider

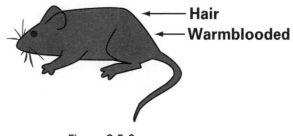

Hair
Warmblooded

Figure 8.5-3

Mouse

Activity 8.6
HOW CAN YOU MAKE A BIRDHOUSE?

(Construction project under teacher supervision)

Materials Needed

- Assorted pieces of wood
- Saw
- Hammer
- Plastic and paper milk cartons
- Assorted nails
- Dowels
- Paper

Procedure

1. Figures 8.6-1 and 8.6-2 show pictures of simple birdhouses.
2. If you would like to construct one, make a drawing (plan) and show it to your teacher.
3. Your teacher will help you gather the materials and build a birdhouse, or take your approved plan home and have someone help you.
4. Share your birdhouse with the class.

For Problem Solvers: Do some serious observation and research and find out what kinds of birds are in your area and what types of birdhouses they seem to prefer. With others who are interested in this activity, build several types of birdhouses. Predict what kinds of birds will be attracted to each, then test your predictions by frequent observation. Also find out which locations birds prefer by placing the same type of birdhouse in two or more locations. In each case, before you actually set out a birdhouse for occupancy, write your predictions of the kinds of birds that will be attracted to each type of birdhouse and which location that bird will prefer. Keep accurate records of your observations Can you outguess the birds?

Share your observations with one another as you complete the activity.

Teacher Information

If there is enough interest, this could become a project for everyone in the classroom. If so, you will need parents or aides to assist.

Don't feel limited to the birdhouses in the pictures. Urge students to be creative in their designs. Remember that birdhouses need to be durable and weatherproof. Also, different styles of birdhouses will attract different birds. The size of the hole, for instance, will help determine the type of bird attracted to the birdhouse. Consult a bird book for specifics. Birds may not move into the houses for some time due to season, scent, location, or other factors.

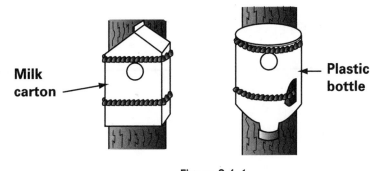

Milk
carton

Plastic
bottle

Figure 8.6-1

Two Birdhouse Designs

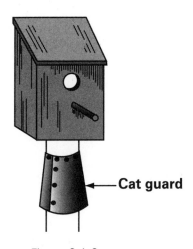

Cat guard

Figure 8.6-2

Birdhouse Design with Cat Guard

Commercial bird feeders and birdhouses are available but should be purchased only if students are unable to construct them. Kits from which birdhouses can be constructed are often available.

If birds are plentiful in your area, birdhouses make wonderful gifts.

INTEGRATING: Language arts, math, art

SKILLS: Observing, inferring, classifying, measuring, predicting, communicating, comparing and contrasting, using space-time relationships, formulating hypotheses, identifying and controlling variables, experimenting, researching

Activity 8.7
WHAT DO WE NEED IN ORDER TO KEEP PETS IN AN AQUARIUM?

(Total-group project)

Materials Needed

- 10-gallon (or larger) aquarium, glass cover, and stand
- Heater
- Thermometer
- Air pump
- Clean gravel
- Sand
- Water plants
- Water
- Snails
- Fish
- Fish food
- Rocks of various sizes and shapes
- Small fish net

Procedure

1. An aquarium is a place in your classroom for aquatic animals. With your teacher's help you can make the aquarium into a comfortable home. Place the aquarium in a sunny, protected place in the room.

2. Decide on the variety of fish you will want to have in your aquarium. Freshwater fish (goldfish varieties) can usually live comfortably without a special heater in most classrooms. Tropical and exotic fish need a carefully controlled environment, so you will need a heater and thermometer. If you choose saltwater fish and don't live near an ocean, your pet store may have salt you can add to fresh water but it is more difficult to maintain.

3. Put about 2.5 cm (1 in.) of clean gravel in the bottom of the aquarium, sloping upward from front to back. Add assorted rocks near the back.

4. Spread about 2.5 cm (1 in.) of clean sand over the gravel slope.

5. Slowly add water (so as not to stir the sand) up to about 5 cm (2 in.) of the top. For freshwater fish, pond water or well water is best. If you use city water, let it stand in open containers for at least 24 hours before adding it to the aquarium (to allow chemicals to disperse into the air).

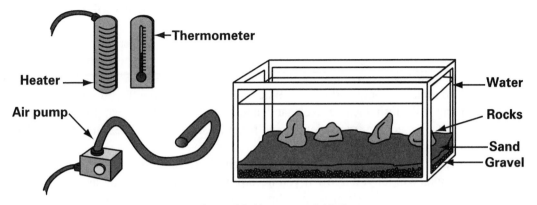

Aquarium with Heater and Air Pump

6. Add green water plants (a variety of six or more). These can be purchased at a pet store and will depend on the kind of fish you choose to keep.

7. If you have chosen to make a freshwater aquarium, all you need to do is add several fish and freshwater snails to keep the tank clean. Put the lid on top. If you have chosen tropical fish, you will need to continue with the following steps.

8. Install the heater and thermometer and wait for the water to stabilize at the desired temperature. (*Note*: Some heaters come with thermostats, but a thermometer is still helpful as a safety check.)

9. Secure the hose from the air pump to a rock on the bottom of the aquarium. Turn it on.

10. Put the tropical fish in your aquarium. Instead of snails you may need to purchase special fish with suction mouths to keep the tank clean. The pet store can provide special instructions for testing the water and feeding fish.

11. You now have a type of "aquatic nature square" in your classroom.

12. Look at the Observation Chart you used to study your outdoor nature square. Using it as a model, design an Observation Chart for your aquarium.

Teacher Information

If you have never constructed an aquarium before, talk to a pet store owner or someone else about the special needs of tropical fish. You may need additional equipment to maintain it properly.

Aquariums with tropical fish are very attractive and interesting, but freshwater or salt-water aquariums (if you are near the ocean) are more representative of water life as it exists. There are several additional advantages to a freshwater aquarium. If it is 10 gallons or larger, it will be nearly balanced and will not require an air pump. "Balanced" means that the plants produce about the same amount of oxygen as the animals use. The animals in turn release enough carbon dioxide for the plants. If you match your fish, snails, and plants properly (this usually takes time), the fish will get food from the plants. The plants will use the waste products of the fish for food to produce new growth, and the snails will keep the whole area clean and tidy.

Occasionally you should remove the glass lid to permit air to get in (or leave a ventilating space), and you may want to add a little fish food to give your pets a treat. An aquarium that is nearly in balance will need a change of water about twice a year (add pond water occasionally to replace evaporated water). When the water is changed, you will need to start at the beginning with fresh, clean gravel, sand, and rocks. Again, use fresh pond water if you can—if you use tapwater, be sure to let it stand for at least 24 hours. The same plant and animal life can be retained.

Periodically have the students assist you in checking the "health" of your aquarium. Usually conditions will let you know if you need more plants, animals, or snails.

Don't be concerned if a green slimy film develops on the top of the water. This is a sign of a healthy aquarium. Probably plants and animals too small to see with the naked eye are also living in the tank.

Freshwater aquariums can also provide a home for tadpoles. When they begin to grow legs, simply transfer them to a combined environment of pond water and land and watch them develop into frogs. Use shallow water and tilt the tank so part of the tank floor is not covered with water. This will assure that the tadpoles can get air when their lungs begin to develop, in case they are not transferred quite soon enough.

INTEGRATING: Language arts, social studies

SKILLS: Observing, inferring, classifying, measuring, predicting, communicating, using space-time relationships, identifying and controlling variables, researching

Activity 8.8
HOW CAN WE KEEP SMALL ANIMALS IN OUR CLASSROOM?

(Total-group project)

Materials Needed

- Aquarium or terrarium (at least 20 gallons)
- Clean gravel
- Clean sand
- Potting soil
- Plants (see "Procedure")
- Assorted rocks, small pieces of wood
- Small, shallow plastic pan
- Heavy wire screen
- Small reptiles or other small animals

Procedure

1. You can keep small animals in your classroom if they have a comfortable place to live. Find a warm, sunny, protected place in your room as a permanent location for your terrarium. Although you may be using the same container, *aquarium* means *water home*, and *terrarium* means *land home*. Be sure it is clean.

2. With your teacher and other class members, choose the kind of animals (reptiles, amphibians, or mammals) you would like to have. If you have enough containers you could make homes for each variety.

3. Use library books to learn about the animals you have chosen and plan a comfortable environment for the animals.

4. Put about 2.5 cm (1 in.) of gravel in the bottom of your terrarium. Add about 2.5 cm (1 in.) of sand on top. Arrange the rocks and pieces of wood throughout the container to provide privacy and shade.

5. Locate the plastic pan near one side. If you have chosen desert animals they will need very little water. If you have chosen turtles or amphibians you should use a water container somewhat deeper that will cover about one third of the bottom. Put several flat rocks in the amphibian or turtle container so the animals will have a place to climb out and "sun."

6. Be sure the pan is easy to remove, as you will need to clean it regularly. Depending on the variety of animal you have chosen, you may need to add a small tray for food.

7. From the study of the animal you have chosen, select small plants that naturally occur in its environment. If you are housing animals that like a moist environment, mix about 2.5 cm (1 in.) of potting soil in the sand.

8. Before you put your animals in their new home, be sure you have a heavy wire covering over the top so your animals cannot climb or jump out.

9. Your terrarium cannot be "balanced" as a fresh water aquarium can be; therefore, your animals will need fresh food and water regularly. The plants will need varying amounts of moisture, too.

10. Put your animals in their new home and watch their behavior. Can you design an Observation Chart to help study them?

Teacher Information

Resource people can be of great help in this study. If aquariums are not available, cardboard or wooden boxes with the top and one side covered with heavy plastic can be used for insects, reptiles, and amphibians. Be sure to provide plenty of air holes covered with screen. Mammals, especially rodents, will gnaw through cardboard or wood and must be housed in glass or metal cages. Use a sieve to clean the sand in the bottom of the cage about once a week. Commercially purchased cages are excellent for temporary housing. They are easy to clean and they reduce the amount of care required.

Housing male and female mammals together can become a problem. If the female becomes pregnant she will need to be separated from the male. Pregnant rodents are not recommended for classroom care and study. During gestation they should not be disturbed for cleaning (especially their nests) and after birth, if frightened or molested, they may eat their young.

If you construct an amphibian environment you will be able to start with tadpoles and watch them change into frogs.

Turtles, newts, and frogs make very good amphibian-reptile pets. Horned lizards, common lizards, tortoises, and small snakes will live together in a desert environment.

Usually it is best to have only one species of mammal. Gerbils, hamsters, and guinea pigs are clean and easy to care for. Wild mice, rats, or mink are not recommended.

Many insects will live together. Spiders (including the gentle tarantula), beetles, and crickets can share the same cage. Praying mantises are very interesting but should be housed alone as they are voracious eaters and also cannibalistic. Books and resource persons can help in your selection of animals.

When your terrariums are complete, have the children list the "daily care" tasks and organize groups with specific time, day, and date assignments.

Live specimens and food can be obtained by collecting and from pet stores and science-supply houses.

If animals are kept in the classroom, some are likely to die there. Teachers need to be aware of the sensitivity of this issue with children. Insects have a short life span. Insects and spiders eat other insects and spiders. Tadpoles have a high mortality rate from egg to frog. Handled properly, these can be valuable learning experiences for children as they observe life's natural processes.

INTEGRATING: Reading, language arts, social studies

SKILLS: Observing, inferring, classifying, measuring, predicting, communicating, using space-time relationships, formulating hypotheses, identifying and controlling variables, researching

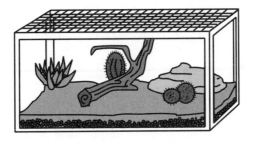

Desert terrarium

Woodland terrarium

Pan of water

Pond terrarium

Activity 8.9
WHAT ORGANISMS LIVE AROUND US THAT ARE TOO TINY TO SEE?

Materials Needed

- Common microscopic organisms, such as euglena and paramecium
- Microscopes
- 9″ × 12″ drawing paper
- Pencil

Procedure

1. There are many tiny living things, too small to see with the naked eye, that live around us. You have already used magnifying lenses to examine some small insects and plants. In your study of birds you might use binoculars. Today we are going to see tiny living things—so tiny that they cannot be seen without microscopes. The following figure shows some of the most common organisms you may see.

2. Across the top of your paper, draw pictures of the organisms in the figure. As you see other organisms in the microscope today, try to make a drawing of them. Put your pictures under the drawings of the ones in the figure they most closely resemble. You are now ready to conduct your inquiry.

3. After you have seen and made drawings of the tiny living things you see, share your findings with the class. How are they alike? How are they different? Which did you like best?

Euglena   **Paramecium**   **Hydra**   **Planaria (worm)**

Drawings of Four Microorganisms

For Problem Solvers: Do some research on microorganisms. Get some water from a pond and with just a drop of water at a time see if you can find some tiny living things in it. Find out what a hay infusion is and prepare one. Using a microscope see how many different kinds of tiny organisms you can find in your hay infusion. Use an encyclopedia or other reference books and identify as many of them as you can.

Are these tiny creatures called animals? Look up *protozoan* in the encyclopedia. What's the difference between animals and protozoa?

Can you figure out a way to measure the length of one of your tiny organisms? Consider this question with others who are interested in these tiny creatures and discuss your plan with your teacher.

Teacher Information

These tiny creatures are no longer classified as animals, as they once were.

It is not necessary to make positive identifications of every organism you find. Use the figure to make general classifications.

Microorganisms are usually present in pond water, the surface of your freshwater aquarium or in a *hay infusion*, which you can make or purchase from a science-supply house. A video on organisms of a pond may be helpful.

Some of the microorganisms you find might move around so fast that it's difficult to keep them in view in the microscope. Try putting a tiny bit of cotton in the drop of water. This will usually corral the little varmints long enough to get a good look at them.

If you invite a specialist to help you, be sure to explain that you are interested only in a simple, general introduction with many visuals. The purpose of this activity is to develop awareness of these tiny creatures, not to learn all about them. The students will encounter courses in later years where they will be able to explore in depth.

An in-depth study of microorganisms could be an enrichment activity for highly motivated students.

INTEGRATING: Language arts, math, art

SKILLS: Observing, inferring, classifying, measuring, communicating, comparing and contrasting, using space-time relationships, identifying and controlling variables, researching

Topic 9: Growing and Changing: Animal Life Cycles

TO THE TEACHER

This section, "Growing and Changing," should follow or be integrated into the preceding section, "Animals." Depending on where you live, the Animals section may be taught in early fall, but in locations where distinct seasons occur, Growing and Changing is best taught in the spring months.

Several of the activities involve the use of live specimens. If you live in an area where you cannot collect caterpillars or tadpoles, you will need to place orders with pet stores or biological science supply houses in January or February. If you order early and specify a later shipping date, most supply houses are happy to cooperate, and they are very good at getting your orders to you at the right time. Be aware that some states require USDA permits for interstate shipment of live animals. The supply catalog will advise you if this is necessary. Animals purchased in local pet stores will already have been approved.

Obtaining, organizing, and filing a wide variety of pictures is essential to quality teaching in the elementary school. In addition to the journals recommended in the appendixes of this book, old biological science supply catalogs obtained from a local high school or college should be of great help. Many are filled with high-quality photographs. Obsolete science textbooks and library books can often be obtained from your school district free of charge. The text material may be out of date, but the pictures usually are not. Some organizations, such as the Audubon Society, sponsor junior organizations for young people.

In some activities in this section, animals that lay eggs with the young hatching and developing outside the female's body are studied. Others utilize animals that retain the fertilized egg inside the mother's body. The terms *hatch* and *born alive* are used in some manner to make this distinction.

Instructions are included for hatching eggs in the classroom. Attempting to show live birth at the elementary level is *not* recommended. Smaller mammals, such as mice or gerbils, should not be disturbed during the gestation time even for cage cleaning. After birth, if mothers are frightened, they might eat their young.

Integrated creative learning activities are suggested throughout this section. Try to include as many as possible.

Activity 9.1
WHERE DO BUTTERFLIES COME FROM?

Materials Needed

- Larva, cocoon, or chrysalis of moth or butterfly
- One copy of Figure 9.1-1 for each student
- Insect cage (see Figure 9.1-2) or butterfly kit from pet store or supply house
- Hand lenses
- Pencils

Procedure

1. Study Figure 9.1-1. It shows the way butterflies and moths develop.

2. There is a new animal in the room in a particular stage of metamorphosis. Look at Figure 9.1-1 and find the stage of development your new animal most closely resembles.

3. If your animal is in the larva or pupa stage, there are usually ways to tell whether the adult will be a moth or a butterfly. Look at Figure 9.1-1 and see if you can find any differences. Beside the picture of the adult, write the name of the variety of insect (moth or butterfly) you think your animal will become.

4. When your insect becomes an adult, it will soon be able to fly. Do you have a good cage for it? Figure 9.1-2 shows several simple cages you can make. Choose one and form a group to construct it.

5. Give your adult insect a name. Use books, pictures, and your own observations to learn all you can about it. Notice how many beautiful ways butterflies are used in art.

6. After a few days, take your butterfly or moth to a sunny place near flowers. Say goodbye to it and set it free.

For Problem Solvers: Make a butterfly net. Find ideas in the encyclopedia or, better yet, create your own design. Consider using nylon stockings or panty hose as the net. You will need a ring to mount it to and a handle. Share your ideas with others, and together you should be able to come up with a dandy design.

Teacher Information

This is a middle- to late-spring activity in many parts of the country. Observing the metamorphosis of a butterfly or moth is an exciting, worthwhile experience for students of all ages. The time it takes to develop from larva to pupa to adult is less than that for a frog. Allow 30 to 45 days; however, the larval stage of caterpillars varies in length. Specimens collected locally are best. You will need to provide ample food and moisture for a period. Your encyclopedia or library books will provide detailed instructions.

Occasionally a student may bring a cocoon or chrysalis to class. If this occurs you may want to try to find a caterpillar to use for comparisons with Figure 9.1-1, butterfly and moth metamorphosis. In the larva stage moth caterpillars are usually hairy or "woolly." Butterfly caterpillars are usually smooth-skinned.

Butterflies form a hard, smooth shell called a chrysalis. Pictures from books may help show the differences. Remember, as with egg hatching, your insect may not spin its cocoon or emerge as an adult during the school day. If you have several specimens, the chance of the children seeing the process is greatly increased. Mortality rate is lower than with tadpoles, but occasionally a caterpillar will die or not emerge from its cocoon or chrysalis. Be patient; never try to help the adult emerge from the pupal stage. The struggle to emerge and the drying out of the wings are part of the natural life process and should not be disturbed. Moths spin cocoons.

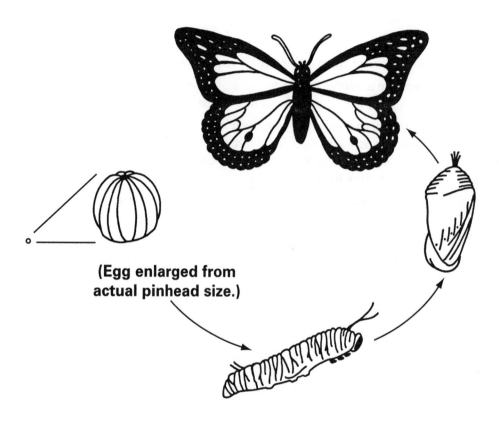

(Egg enlarged from actual pinhead size.)

Figure 9.1-1

Butterfly or Moth Metamorphosis

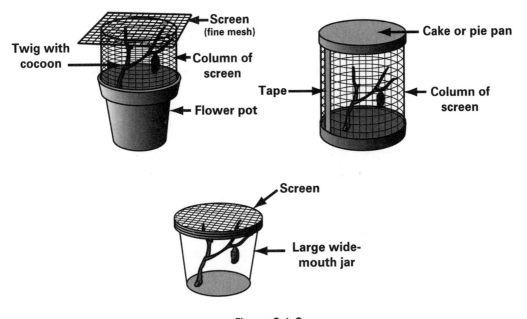

Figure 9.1-2

Homemade Insect Cages

The development of a butterfly or moth is so exciting, beautiful, and "mysterious" that every child should experience it at some time during his or her school years. Even if the activity is repeated several times over the years, students will view it with different backgrounds of experience, but always with great anticipation and excitement.

If you live in an area where butterflies are not readily available, larva, and even complete kits with cages and food, can be ordered from biological science supply houses at a very reasonable price. However, if possible we recommend that you collect, house, and care for local insects.

Books, pictures, and stories about butterflies are plentiful. Be sure to use them to enrich this experience. Music, art, poetry, and creative movement can be included in your learning activities.

Collecting, killing, and mounting insects is not recommended for early elementary grades.

INTEGRATING: Reading, music, art, dance

SKILLS: Observing, inferring, classifying, predicting, communicating, comparing and contrasting, using space-time relationships, formulating hypotheses, identifying and controlling variables, experimenting, researching

Activity 9.2
WHAT IS WORMY?

(Small-group activity)

Materials Needed

- Mealworms in container labeled "Mealworms"
- Earthworms in container labeled "Earthworms"
- Waxed paper
- Figure 9.1-1
- Writing paper
- Pencils
- Hand lenses
- Tablespoons
- Pie tins or small cake pans

Procedure

1. Have you ever heard someone say, "Oh, it has worms in it?" On your paper write the names of things they might be talking about. Most of the items on your list are probably things humans eat. What is similar about them?

2. Line a pie tin or cake pan with waxed paper.

3. Use a spoon to transfer one animal from the container marked "Earthworms" and one from the container marked "Mealworms."

4. Use your hand lens to study both worms. Make a simple drawing of each.

5. On your paper write ways they are alike and ways they are different. Compare such things as size, color, how they move, legs, head, eyes, mouth, and any other similarities or differences you can find.

6. Compare your pictures and description of your worms with Figure 9.1-1.

7. One of your worms is not a real worm at all. Can you tell which one? How?

8. Share the findings of your group with your teacher and the class.

For Problem Solvers: Which can move faster—a snail, an earthworm, or a mealworm? How could you find out?

From what you have learned, can you answer this question: Is the silkworm really a worm?

Teacher Information

There are many more known species of insects in the world than all other species of animals and plants combined. Many species go through a complete metamorphosis where the larvae bear some resemblance to true worms.

Many insects lay their eggs on or in living or once-living material including plants and wool. When the eggs hatch, the larva feed on the material upon which they were laid. "Wormy" apples are actually apples that have housed the larva or maggot stage of an insect.

Maggots are legless, soft-bodied larvae usually found in decaying material. Larvae from the housefly, the mosquito, and relatives are common throughout the world. We often try to control harmful insects at the larva stage (for example, a lid on a garbage can or treating standing water may kill more flies or mosquitoes than you could swat in a lifetime).

A mealworm is the larva of one of several grain-eating beetles. They are available at most pet stores because they are used as food for larger animals (fish, amphibians, and lizards). They are easily stored in a can with bran flakes or a similar food substance. Add moisture to the can occasionally and dispose of the contents at least once during the school year.

Your earthworm is a true segmented worm and belongs to a completely different group of animals (see your encyclopedia for further information).

INTEGRATING: Reading, language arts

SKILLS: Observing, inferring, classifying, measuring, communicating, using space-time relationships, formulating hypotheses, identifying and controlling variables, experimenting, researching

Activity 9.3
HOW LONG DO ANIMALS LIVE?

Materials Needed

- Chart of animal life spans (see the following illustration)
- Resource people

Procedure

1. Look at the following illustration. It shows the average length of life of some common animals. On the left side of the diagram from bottom to top are numbers of years. Across the page are drawings of different animals. Find the animals with the shortest and the longest life spans.

2. Use your chart to discuss with your teacher and the class the following questions:

   a. Why do some animals live longer than others?

   b. How do scientists determine an average age?

   c. Why has man's life expectancy increased in recent years?

3. Invite some older people to visit your class. Find out why they think they have lived as long as they have.

Teacher Information

Animal life spans and cycles vary greatly. Some complete a generation in hours, weeks, or months. Others take many years to mature. Life cycles of many animals are focused on continuation of the species. When the reproductive process is complete the animal dies. Natural controls such as predators, available food supplies, and other environmental factors also play a part.

Although many animals have different adaptations and use different methods for survival, man is the only animal to seek consciously to prolong life. For this reason, too, domesticated animals tend to live longer than their "cousins" in a natural or wild state.

Students may want to add animals to their life span chart. An encyclopedia or other reference book will usually give life expectancies. Microscopic organisms are not included in this activity.

Be sure to select the older visitors with care. Conduct a personal interview first and if possible suggest some specific topics to discuss. Children often have more in common with older people than with people in the "middle" years. With care this activity can be a very rich learning experience, and perhaps form lasting bonds.

INTEGRATING: Language arts, social studies

SKILLS: Communicating, comparing and contrasting, using space-time relationships, formulating hypotheses

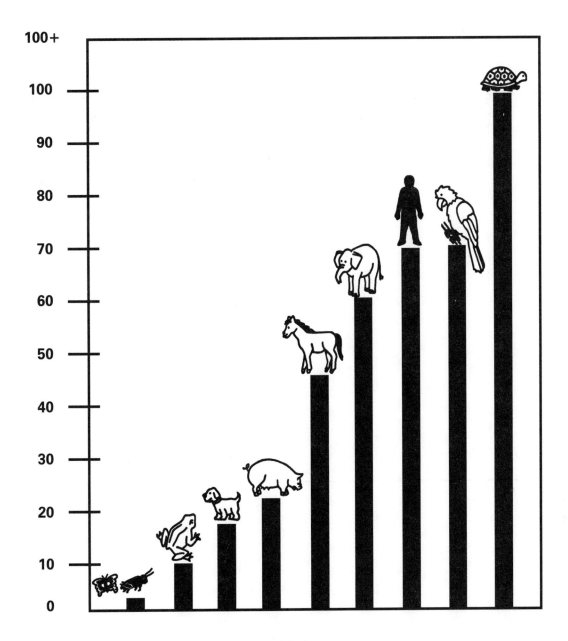

Animal life Spans

185

Topic 10: Animal Adaptations

TO THE TEACHER

The following activities are examples of some specific ways animals adapt to their environment. Feathers and birds are used frequently in these activities because they are common even in large cities and suburban areas, and many types of adaptations are evident. Feathers collected from wild birds should be carefully examined before use. Check on laws pertaining to the possession of feathers before collecting any of them.

The importance of a picture collection is emphasized in the general introduction to this book. This section relies heavily on the use of pictures. Older students might be interested in starting picture collections of their own.

Some household tools used in some of these activities are sharp and potentially dangerous. Careful discretion and close teacher supervision is recommended.

People are the most adaptable animals on earth. Teachers have frequent need to adapt. As you read and prepare to teach this section, feel free to adapt it in any way you choose to meet the needs of your students and the conditions of the environment in which they live. Most important, adapt this study according to your needs, special skills, and knowledge.

Activity 10.1
WHAT IS ADAPTATION?

(Small-group discussion)

Materials Needed

- Pictures of people living, working, and playing in different climates
- Newsprint
- Pencils

Procedure

1. *Adaptation* in plants and animals refers to the way they can adjust or change to be able to live where and how they do. Many animals and plants can live only in certain places. People have made adaptations so they can live for periods of time almost anywhere. Discuss with your teacher some of the adaptations (adjustments) that have been made by you and others to enable you to be comfortable in your classroom today. List some important ones on the board.

2. Divide into groups of four or five and look at the pictures of ways people adapt to live, work, and play all over the world. Make a list of some ways humans are different from other animals in their ability to adapt.

3. From your pictures, choose the most interesting adaptations and share them with the class.

For Problem Solvers: Find out about plans for current and future space exploration. What adaptations will be required to live for an extended time in space stations?

Select a favorite animal. Study its habits and lifestyle in depth and identify as many of its adaptations as you can.

Teacher Information

This can be a very simple activity related to seasons for younger children.

With older students, you may want to relate this activity to your social studies and include historical adaptations, such as those of Eskimos, Indians, pioneers of the past, and primitive people of today. Geography, weather, climate, and food offer almost limitless possibilities for illustrating the human ability to adapt.

For centuries, people have dreamed of exploring and colonizing outer space. Students who have a background in the study of the solar system may choose to explore this topic for enrichment.

Plan to have 50 or more pictures showing homes, food, transportation, recreation, clothing, and everyday activities.

INTEGRATING: Reading, language arts, social studies

SKILLS: Observing, inferring, classifying, communicating, comparing and contrasting, using space-time relationships, formulating hypotheses, identifying and controlling variables, researching

Activity 10.2
HOW DO ANIMALS MOVE?

(Small-group activity)

Materials Needed

- Pictures of animals that move in different ways (swimming, walking, hopping, gliding, crawling, flying, climbing) and of animals that don't move, such as barnacles
- Live animals in aquarium, cages, and terrarium
- Paper
- Pencils

Procedure

1. Look at the live animals and the pictures of animals in your room. Can you tell how each one moves about? Can you find any that don't seem to move?

2. Write the names of the animals on the left side of your paper. Next to their names, write the ways they move (remember, some move in different ways). Try to think of more than one word to describe their movement, for example, fish swim, but they also wiggle and swish; snakes crawl, but they also slither and glide; cats walk, run, crawl, creep, climb, stalk, and pounce. How many words can you find for each animal?

3. Think of the ways you move. Look at your list of animal movements. Underline the ones you can imitate.

4. Are there any movements you can do as well or better than some other animal (hint: pick up a pencil or tie a shoelace)? Why are you able to do these things better?

5. Have a class discussion about why you think animals move as they do.

Teacher Information

Younger students may enjoy trying to imitate the movements of animals. Older students can play animal movement charades, in which they guess the animal being portrayed. Animal movements may also inspire creative dancing. Some cultures imitate animal movements with costumes, music, and dance.

Animal movements are most often based on their environment (water, land, or both), method of obtaining food, courtship rituals, and defense or protection. Some animals seem to dance or play just for fun.

When size and proportions are taken into consideration, animals that specialize in a particular type of movement can perform that movement far better and more efficiently than people (even remaining still). Thanks to the opposed thumb, the movement people can make better than any other animal is grasping. This has enabled people to be the best tool users and, along with their ability to think and reason, to create many technical and mechanical adaptations to compete with the specialized movements of other animals.

Don't forget the many mechanical robots that are popular as children's toys. You might plan a "robot day" when everyone is invited to bring his or her favorite doll or mechanical animal toy and explain how it works. No matter how well designed, mechanical toys cannot perform animal movements nearly as well as the animal itself.

INTEGRATING: Language arts, social studies, art

SKILLS: Observing, inferring, classifying, communicating, comparing and contrasting, formulating hypotheses, identifying and controlling variables

Activity 10.3
HOW DO SOME ANIMALS COMMUNICATE?

(Partners or small-group activity)

Materials Needed

- Paper
- Pencil

Procedure

1. We usually think of communicating as ways of giving or receiving information or conveying emotions and feelings by talking and listening. Listening and watching (movies, radio, television) or drawing and looking at pictures are also usual ways people communicate. Can you think of any other ways?

2. In step 1, did you add reading, which you are doing now? Did you remember gestures, too? On your paper, write as many ways as you can think of that people communicate.

3. Scientists believe that many animals communicate in different ways, but only man has been able to create a vocabulary of many words to communicate ideas. If you own or know a household pet, discuss the ways it communicates with you without using words. Does it seem to understand what you say? Write down as many of these ways as you can.

4. With partners or in small groups, pretend none of you can hear or speak. Without drawing pictures or making any sound, take turns describing your favorite game or toy.

5. You probably found your best way of communicating without making sound was with gestures. Many people who cannot speak or hear learn gestures called sign language or "signing" to communicate. List on your paper some animals that use gestures or signals to communicate (Hint: How does a dog show it is friendly?).

6. What are some ways people communicate today that they could not do before the invention of the computer?

For Problem Solvers: Much research has been done, and is being done, on ways various forms of animals communicate with each other. Use your references and learn all you can about what has been discovered through such research. What about the monkey family, and the whale family? What about ants, bees, and other insects? Other animals?

Teacher Information

In addition to the opposed thumb, the abilities to create and use oral language and pictures seem to be unique to people. There seems to be little doubt that other higher animals such as apes can reason and think, but only people are known to have developed a complex language with which to express ideas.

Apes and chimpanzees have been successfully trained to use symbols and sign language (see *National Geographic*, January 1985).

Most other animals seem to use communication instinctively to express warning, fear, anger, recognition, and food gathering, or as mating calls and signals. The famous "bee dance" is described in your encyclopedia. Ants also have methods for communicating the location of food. Most insect communities provide studies of specialization and ways animals within a species are adapted to specialized roles. Some sea mammals, such as porpoises and whales, seem to have complex communication systems that scientists have, so far, been unable to decode.

Language has enabled people to use the environment to adapt, create, and express as no other animal can. As people continue to adapt the computer to every phase of life the implications for computers seem endless. For sheer joy of expression, however, many people believe that the infinitely varied song of the humpback whale has no equal.

INTEGRATING: Reading, language arts, social studies

SKILLS: Observing, inferring, classifying, communicating, comparing and contrasting, using space-time relationships, formulating hypotheses, identifying and controlling variables, experimenting, researching

Activity 10.4
HOW DO SEASONS AFFECT ANIMAL ADAPTATIONS?

Materials Needed

- Pictures of butterfly, migratory bird (Arctic tern, Canada goose) local year-round bird, squirrel, rabbit, earthworm, snake, bear, deer, elk, whale, and pictures of people from Activity 10.1
- Map of the world
- Globe
- Cards labeled "Hibernate," "Migrate," "Adapt"

Procedure

1. Place the three cards at the top of the table. Discuss the meaning of each word with your teacher.

2. Look at the map and the globe of the earth. Usually there is less seasonal change near the middle, or the *equator*. As you travel north or south toward the poles, seasonal changes become greater. Find the place where you live. How far are you from the equator, and from the North Pole or South Pole?

3. Oceans and other large bodies of water affect land temperature. Water does not change in temperature as rapidly as land does. If you live near an ocean, changes in seasons may not be as great. Does a large body of water affect your climate? How?

4. Study the pictures of animals. See how many pictures you can match with the three cards to show how these animals adapt to seasonal change.

5. With your teacher and other members of the group, discuss your reasons for grouping the pictures the way you did. Why do you think some animals migrate, while others stay and adapt to seasonal change?

For Problem Solvers: Do people migrate? Think about people you know who move from one place to another throughout the year. Write a list of examples of people you know or can find out about.

Teacher Information

Animals have different ways of adapting to seasonal change, mostly due to the availability of food. Some hibernate in a completely resting stage. Some animals, such as bears, increase their rest and reduce their level of activity but do not completely hibernate.

Many animals remain active in the same area year-round and utilize whatever food is available.

Animal migration is a fascinating area of study. You may find high student interest and extend your study beyond the information introduced here.

In past times caribou, buffalo, and reindeer existed in great numbers. As these animals migrated with seasonal change, men who depended on them for their existence (food and clothing) also migrated.

INTEGRATING: Language arts, social studies

SKILLS: Observing, inferring, classifying, measuring, predicting, communicating, comparing and contrasting, using space-time relationships, formulating hypotheses, experimenting, researching

Activity 10.5
HOW DO ANIMALS ADAPT TO SEASONAL CHANGE?

(Small-group activity)

Materials Needed

- Pictures, map, and globe from Activity 10.4
- Picture of Arctic tern (if not in above collection)
- String
- Masking tape
- Scissors

Procedure

1. Find the picture of the Arctic tern. It is most famous as a world traveler. Locate Greenland on the globe. Many baby terns are hatched here in late June or early July. Place a piece of masking tape here.

2. Within a few weeks the terns are ready to begin their migration. Use the globe, a 50-cm (20-in.) piece of string, and a piece of masking tape to mark their journey.

3. After leaving Greenland, they fly to the west coast of Europe. Stretch your string and tape it from Greenland to the west coast of France, Spain, or Portugal.

4. From this point they fly down the west coast of Africa. Stretch your string and tape it to at least two points near the top and bottom of Africa's west coast.

5. From a point near the southwest part of Africa they make a long journey over the south Atlantic and the Antarctic Ocean to the crusted ice of Antarctica. Stretch your string across the oceans to Antarctica and tape it there. Because the seasons are opposite in the Northern and Southern Hemispheres of our earth, it is summer in the south when it is winter in the north.

6. Terns spend several months in Antarctica, during which they may circle the entire continent. Make a circle with your string around Antarctica.

7. Look at the string path from Greenland to Antarctica on your globe. This marks half the distance a tern flies each year. By May, winter is beginning in Antarctica and the tern returns to Greenland over approximately the same route. Mark or cut the string where the tern's journey ends in Antarctica. Remove the string from the globe. Measure the length of the string and cut another piece twice as long. This represents (stands for) the total distance a tern may travel each year.

8. Wrap the longer piece of string around the globe at the equator. Then wrap it around the globe crossing both the North Pole and the South Pole. Can you see why we call terns world travelers?

9. Other animals in the pictures travel shorter distances, and for different reasons. Some birds in the United States and Europe migrate east and west rather than north and south. Why?

For Problem Solvers: Choose the picture of one animal that migrates. Use your encyclopedia and books from the media center to find out as much as you can about the animal you chose. Share your investigation with the class.

Find out about animals that migrate very short distances.

Teacher Information

Availability of globes may limit the size of groups. Try to borrow as many globes as possible so students can work out the problems themselves.

Some birds in Europe, North America, and other parts of the world migrate east and west rather than north and south because they "summer" inland and "winter" near the coast where it is warmer. Ornithologists are not certain how birds navigate or "home." Theories include the use of stars, the earth's magnetism, landmarks, and combinations of these. Their ability to find a specific location on the earth is amazing, and they do it even in great numbers without the help of traffic controllers!

INTEGRATING: Reading, math, social studies

SKILLS: Observing, inferring, classifying, measuring, predicting, communicating, comparing and contrasting, using space-time relationships, formulating hypotheses, identifying and controlling variables, researching

Activity 10.6
CAN YOU DESIGN A BETTER BIRD?

(Teacher-assisted small groups or partners)

Materials Needed

- Pictures of birds in flight, on land, on water
- Paper and straw feathers
- Balloons of different sizes and shapes
- Small plastic foam balls
- Plastic drinking straws
- Colored construction paper
- Cloth or nylon stockings
- String
- Strong white glue
- Pencils and crayons
- Scissors
- Newsprint
- Wire coat hangers (optional)

Procedure

1. Choose a picture of a bird you like. On the table are materials to construct a bird of your own.

2. With your partner or group, make a plan for a bird made of balloons, plastic foam balls, paper, straws, and household utensils.

3. On a sheet of newsprint draw and color a picture of what you think your bird will look like. This will be your construction plan. Be sure to decide whether your bird will be flying, standing, walking, sitting (perching), or swimming.

4. Balloons and plastic foam balls will make good bodies and heads. Straws can be used for feather parts, legs, and feet. If a household utensil is not satisfactory, you may want to make the beak or bill out of something else. Remember, you will need to make many feathers of different colors. You may want to share your plan with your teacher before you begin.

5. After your bird is finished, share it with the class.

6. Give your bird a name. On a piece of paper write its name, what it eats, where it lives, and why it is special.

7. Make an "aviary" for all the birds in your class. Invite visitors to see it.

Teacher Information

This activity could be used at the end of your study of animal adaptation. You will need many paper feathers. If different sizes and colors are cut out from a pattern in advance, much time can be saved. Students may need help in forming the tail, as its shape and construction are often not as obvious as they are for wings.

Coat-hanger wire can be used as rigid supports for the wings of flying birds. If you use coat-hanger wire, be sure to cover the sharp ends with tape (saves on balloons).

No matter how tightly you seal them, balloons will gradually lose air. Inflate them last and plan to have your birds on display for only a few days. If you care to invest the time, the balloons can be covered with papier-mâché to increase the longevity of your birds.

INTEGRATING: Art

SKILLS: Observing, inferring, classifying, measuring, communicating, comparing and contrasting, identifying and controlling variables

Topic 11: Body Systems

TO THE TEACHER

This section provides opportunities for students to learn about themselves. Activities involve both the muscular and skeletal systems of the body. Students can discover and learn a great deal about their own body structure by studying the bones and muscles of animals. These parts are usually available from the local meat market. Hair, nails, skin, and lung capacity are also dealt with in the activities of this section.

The teacher should invite resource people into the classroom at appropriate times to enrich the experience. Along with the sections "Health and Nutrition" and "The Five Senses," the study of this section provides many excellent opportunities to explore the world of work with respect to the health services occupations and professions.

In a study of the body, the handicapped should be recognized as normal people for whom certain abilities are limited. There is such a broad range of ability among the non-handicapped, and such a broad range among the handicapped, that it is sometimes difficult to distinguish between the two. It is hoped that in the study of this section physical differences will be recognized and treated as normal. We are all different. Being different is normal. It should be noted and stressed, however, that we are more alike than different.

We suggest that the teacher scan all activities in the section before beginning its use in the classroom, taking note of materials required. This will aid in making necessary advance preparations.

Activity 11.1
HOW CAN YOU SEE YOUR PULSE?

Materials Needed

- Large thumbtacks
- Used wooden kitchen match

Procedure

1. Carefully insert the point of the thumbtack into the end of a wooden match. The match should extend vertically from the thumbtack.
2. Rest your hand, palm up, on a flat surface.
3. Using the thumbtack as a base, place the match in an upright position on your wrist.
4. Move the match to different positions and observe it.
5. What happened? Why?
6. Run in place for one minute.
7. Repeat the activity. Was there a difference?

Teacher Information

Most students have had their pulse taken at some time. Often they don't understand why or what the doctor or nurse is doing.

A wooden match placed on the wrist, especially in an area in approximate line with the index finger, should move back and forth noticeably.

The pulse is difficult to locate in some people. In some cases medical personnel may use the throat. These differences are normal.

Pulse rate varies from one individual to another, and even for the same person at different times.

INTEGRATING: Physical education

SKILLS: Observing, inferring, measuring, communicating, using space-time relationships, identifying and controlling variables

Activity 11.2
WHAT IS A BLOOD-PRESSURE CUFF?

(Teacher demonstration and supervised partners or small groups)

Materials Needed

• Blood-pressure cuff with gauge

Procedure

1. Examine the blood-pressure cuff. Most of you have seen an instrument similar to this. Medical personnel use it to help them *monitor* (watch) your heart and circulatory system. Identify the cloth cuff, the rubber bulb and tube, and the gauge.

2. Locate the screw knob below the gauge. It regulates the pressure (amount of air) in the cuff. The rubber bulb will pump air into the cloth cuff. By turning the knob, you can control the amount of air in the cuff.

3. Lay the cuff flat on a table. Use the bulb and knob to practice pumping and releasing air from it. *Don't pump it too full or you may damage it.*

4. Study the gauge. It has a dial with numbers on it and a needle that tells the amount of pressure you have pumped into the cuff. Practice using and reading the gauge.

5. Have your partner wrap the long, wide strip of cloth around your upper arm (above the elbow) and fasten it. Be sure the gauge and bulb are on the outside so you can see and touch them.

6. With a partner, practice pumping and releasing air from the cuff on your arms. Be sure to watch the gauge. As the air is released, notice that you can feel a pumping sensation in your arm. Be careful not to pump the air in the cuff so tight that it hurts. Begin to release the pressure at once. *Never leave a tight cuff in place on your arm.*

Teacher Information

This activity should begin with a teacher demonstration and with careful supervision throughout. Circulation to the arm should not be cut off for more than a few seconds. If pressure in the cuff is too great, delicate blood vessels could be damaged.

The main objective of this activity is to show how scientists use instruments to help provide information they need. In some ways it is analogous to the gauges and dials in your automobile.

Some of the anxieties many of us have about going to the doctor can be reduced through an understanding of the why and how of many of the instruments used. Many pediatricians today understand this concept and attempt to allay children's fear. School activities such as this should help support the efforts of parents and medical personnel.

When students understand how a stethoscope and blood-pressure cuff work, invite a doctor, nurse, or medical technician to show how to take blood pressure and explain what it means.

INTEGRATING: Physical education

SKILLS: Observing, measuring, communicating, using space-time relationships

Activity 11.3
HOW DO THE BODY SYSTEMS WORK TOGETHER?

Materials Needed

- Bicycle

Procedure

1. Examine the bicycle and explain how it works. For each part that moves, tell what makes it move. How do the different parts depend on one another?

2. Look at your body and tell what parts you think depend on other parts.

3. Bend down and pick something off the floor. How did your hand depend on your arm, your arm depend on your shoulders, your shoulders depend on your back, your back depend on your legs, and your legs depend on your feet?

4. Compare the way your body parts depend on one another and work together with the way the bicycle parts depend on one another and work together.

For Problem Solvers: Find a picture of the body's internal organs and study it. From this, can you add to your explanation of parts of the body that depend on one another?

Find a picture that shows the muscular system and the skeletal system. Tell how you think the muscles, bones, and tendons work together.

Teacher Information

Every part of the body depends in some way on many, many other parts of the body. Point out that the control center for all of the body parts is the brain. The "brain" of the bicycle is the person riding it.

Consider making similar comparisons with other machinery in addition to the bicycle, such as a typewriter, pencil sharpener, door latch, and so forth. If someone in the class knows something about automobiles, this person could be asked to explain some of its interdependent systems. This might be a good time to invite a resource person to the classroom, or for a student to do some research and report findings to the class.

INTEGRATING: Physical education

SKILLS: Observing, inferring, communicating, comparing and contrasting

Activity 11.4
WHAT IS YOUR LUNG CAPACITY?

 Take home and do with family and friends.

Materials Needed

- Gallon bottle
- Sink or large pan
- Tubing
- Soda straw (short piece)
- Measuring cup
- Water
- Masking tape

Procedure

1. A bottle with a small opening, such as a cider or vinegar bottle, will work best.

2. Put at least 5 cm (2 in.) of water in the sink.

3. Fill the bottle completely with water.

4. Cover the top of the bottle, turn it over, and stand it upside down in the sink with the opening in the water. When you uncover the opening, no air should enter the jug.

5. Tip the bottle slightly to the side and insert one end of the tube into the opening of the bottle.

6. Have your partner hold the bottle upright while you do steps 7 and 8.

7. Take a deep breath and blow through the tube, emptying the air from your lungs as completely as you can into the bottle.

8. Mark the water level on the bottle with a piece of tape.

9. Empty the bottle, turn it right side up, and use the measuring cup to measure the amount of water required to fill it up to your mark. This is the amount of air you blew into the bottle. It is the vital capacity of your lungs.

10. Repeat the activity for your partner and for others if they wish. Compare and compute the average lung capacity of those who participate.

For Problem Solvers: Conduct a survey of the class and find out what types and amounts of physical exercise each group participates in. Study this information, compare it with the information you have about lung capacity, and decide if you think exercise has an effect on lung capacity. Discuss your information with the class. Do you think singing is an exercise?

Measure the height of class members. Compare height with lung capacity. Do taller people tend to have a greater lung capacity than shorter people?

Measuring Lung Capacity

Teacher Information

This is a valuable activity for practice in measuring a volume of air and in getting acquainted with the body. The word "displace" could become a meaningful new vocabulary word as students observe the displacement of water by air. Have some of your problem solvers investigate the amount and types of physical exercise in which each group member participates. Consider that singing is a very good exercise for the lungs. Then search for correlations between lung capacity and exercise. Someone else could measure the height of each person and search for a correlation between height and lung capacity.

The lung capacity measured in this activity is called the vital lung capacity. It is less than the total lung capacity because some residual air remains in the lungs after exhaling as much as possible.

INTEGRATING: Math, physical education

SKILLS: Observing, inferring, classifying, measuring, predicting, communicating, comparing and contrasting, using space-time relationships, formulating hypotheses, identifying and controlling variables, experimenting, researching

Activity 11.5
HOW DOES OUR SKIN PROTECT US?

Materials Needed

- Four apples
- Straight pin
- Alcohol
- Four sheets of paper
- Cotton swab or paper towel
- Pencil
- Writing paper

Procedure

1. Lay out the four sheets of paper on a table or a shelf. Label the papers A, B, C, and D. Wash your hands carefully .

2. Wash the four apples and place one apple on each paper. Let the labels on the papers identify the apples. You will notice that apple D remains untouched from this point on.

3. Use straight pins to puncture four holes in apple B and four holes in apple C.

4. Have someone with unwashed hands rub his or her hands around on apples A, B, and C, including the punctured areas of apples B and C.

5. Use the cotton swab or paper towel to apply rubbing alcohol to the punctured areas of apple C.

6. Leave all four apples in place, unhandled, for seven days. Each day, examine (but don't touch) the apples and write a description of any changes you observe.

7. After seven days, compare the four apples. Consider the possible effect of the rubbing with dirty hands, the punctures, and the applications of alcohol.

8. Why did we use apple D?

9. Compare the apple skin to your own skin. What can you say about what you observed with the apples?

Teacher Information

Apple D was washed and left untouched to serve as a control. This is an opportunity to stress the importance of the use of controls in many experiments, and the ease of including a control.

The apple skin protects the apple in much the same way as our own skin protects us. This should be evident in comparing apples A and D. When foreign substances do penetrate the skin, such as through an open wound, the importance of using an antiseptic should be evident by comparing apples B and C.

SKILLS: Observing, inferring, classifying, predicting, communicating, using space-time relationships, formulating hypotheses, identifying and controlling variables, experimenting

Activity 11.6
HOW DOES THE SKIN HELP REGULATE BODY TEMPERATURE?

Materials Needed

- Water

Procedure

1. Wet your finger and blow on it. How does it feel?

2. Wet a spot on your arm and blow on it. How does it feel?

3. Think about when you first get out of a shower or a bathtub. How do you feel while you are wet? Do you feel better after you are dry?

4. Think about times you perspire. What do you think the perspiration accomplishes?

For Problem Solvers: See what you can learn about evaporative coolers. Check your encyclopedia and talk to people who use evaporative coolers (sometimes called "swamp coolers") on their homes. Think about how the operation of evaporative coolers compares with perspiration. Share your information and ideas with your group.

Teacher Information

Let students discuss their responses to the above questions. Evaporation is a cooling process. When the body perspires, the evaporation of the moisture cools the skin, helping to control body temperature.

If some of the students have been around horses, they will know that when a horse runs it perspires. Some might also know, from experience or from their reading, that pigs are attracted to water holes on hot days. Pigs do not perspire very much, and this seems to be their way of getting the advantage of the cooling effect of evaporation. Many homes in dry climates are cooled by evaporation coolers, which operate on the same principle. Air is blown through water-soaked filters and the evaporative action cools the air, which in turn cools the home.

The skin helps control body temperature in other ways, too. Have students recall how flushed their faces become when they are hot. This occurs as blood vessels expand, allowing more of the heated blood to flow into the skin to be cooled. Then have them think about the "goose bumps" that form on their skin when they become cold. These occur as blood vessels constrict, closing pores tightly to prevent body heat from escaping.

INTEGRATING: Reading, language arts, social studies

SKILLS: Observing, inferring, classifying, measuring, predicting, communicating, using space-time relationships, formulating hypotheses, identifying and controlling variables, experimenting, researching

Activity 11.7
WHAT DO OUR BONES DO FOR US?

Materials Needed

- Model of a human skeleton

Procedure

1. Examine the skeleton model.

2. Point to where the heart would be located if included in this model.

3. What bones do you see that surround the heart and protect it?

4. What other organs can you think of that are protected by bones? Point to them on your own body and point to where they would be if they were included in this model.

5. Notice how the backbone is constructed. Feel the separate bones in your own back. Why are there so many instead of just one long backbone?

6. Examine the arm and leg bones in the model. Notice how strong they are and where they bend. How do the joints help us?

7. Look at the hands and feet. How many of these bones can you find in your own hands and feet?

Teacher Information

Although some students get an eerie feeling looking at a skeleton, the experience will help them to realize what they really are like beneath the skin. Some of the most obvious functions of the skeletal structure become evident as one examines a model of a human skeleton. Our bones support the flesh and give it shape. Joints are conveniently located to allow the body to bend. Many of the vital organs (heart, lungs, brain) are enclosed in protective coverings of bone.

SKILLS: Observing, classifying, communicating

Activity 11.8
HOW CAN DOCTORS TELL IF AND WHERE A BONE IS BROKEN?

Materials Needed

- X-rays of broken and unbroken bones

Procedure

1. Hold the X-ray films up to the window, one at a time, and compare.

2. Can you tell which bone is broken?

3. Do you see any cracked bones?

4. Why do you think the doctor puts a cast on arms and legs when bones are broken?

5. What do you think might happen if an unqualified person moves someone who has been involved in an accident?

For Problem Solvers: Arrange to visit with an X-ray technician who works in a hospital emergency facility. Ask this person to tell you about some of the common types of injuries that come in, from accidents in the home. Share these with your group and discuss things you might do to decrease the risk of accidental injury in your home.

Consider asking your friendly X-ray technician to visit your class and answer questions about bicycle safety and safety at home, at school, and when participating in certain recreational activities (swimming, hiking, and four-wheeling, for instance).

Teacher Information

Before beginning, ask if anyone in the class has ever broken a bone.

X-rays should be available at a hospital or doctors' clinic if you ask ahead of time and request that some be saved for use in class. Discuss the above questions. Ask students to consider question 5 in terms of a possible broken leg bone, arm bone, or rib bone. You might also wish to discuss it with respect to broken backbones, although this deals with very different and more technical issues.

INTEGRATING: Language arts, social studies

SKILLS: Observing, inferring, communicating

Activity 11.9
HOW IS A SPLINT APPLIED TO A BROKEN BONE?

Materials Needed

- Newspapers
- Several strips of rags at least 5 cm (2 in.) wide and 60 cm (2 ft.) long

Procedure

1. Pretend your leg bone is in one piece and it is not supposed to bend at the knee. Let the knee represent a break in the bone.

2. Have your partner use newspapers and rag strips to make a splint for your leg. Several sections of newspapers should be wrapped around the leg to make it stiff. A bone must not bend at a break, so be sure it is tied securely. It must not be so tight that it stops the flow of blood.

3. Try walking. Can you get yourself up? Does the leg feel that it would remain stiff so the bone could heal properly?

4. Trade places and make a splint for your partner's leg.

5. Have your partner stand up and test your splint to see if it feels secure.

Teacher Information

In this activity students practice making a splint that will hold the bone securely without shutting off the blood supply. A first-aid manual, such as a Boy Scout First Aid Merit Badge booklet, would be an excellent resource to have for reference on splint making, but let students try to accomplish the task with minimal assistance.

SKILLS: Observing, communicating

Activity 11.10
HOW DO VOLUNTARY AND INVOLUNTARY MUSCLES DIFFER?

Materials Needed

- Mirror

Procedure

1. Do the following:

   a. Close one hand and open it.

   b. Lift one foot and put it down.

2. Did these muscles move because you decided to move them? Do they ever move other than when you decide to move them?

3. Do the following:

   a. Look in the mirror and watch your eyes. Notice the size of the pupils (black spot in the middle). Shade one eye with your hand as you observe the pupil.

   b. Put your hand over your heart and feel it beat.

4. Did the size of the pupil change? Did you decide to change it? Can you change the size of the pupil without changing the light? Can you make your heart beat just when you want it to, or make it beat faster or slower?

5. How does your control over the muscles you used in step 1 compare with your control over the muscles in step 3?

6. Now do the following:

   a. Look at your eyes in the mirror for 30 seconds. Did they blink? Do they blink even if you don't decide to make them blink? Can you make them blink faster or more slowly?

   b. Notice how fast you are breathing. Does this happen even if you don't think about it? Can you breathe faster or more slowly if you want to?

7. Compare what you did in steps 1, 3, and 6. How do they compare in the amount of control you have?

For Problem Solvers: Make a list of voluntary actions and involuntary actions. Make a third list that includes actions that are sometimes voluntary and sometimes involuntary. Compare and discuss your list with others who are doing this activity.

Teacher Information

Students will discover some body movements are controlled by voluntary muscles (step 1) and some by involuntary muscles (step 3). Still other muscles are both voluntary and involuntary (step 6). For instance, we can speed up our breathing or the blinking of the eyes, but if we don't think about it, automatic mechanisms take over. Breathing and blinking go on without conscious effort on our part. We can also delay these actions temporarily, but if we interfere too long, the involuntary actions will override our efforts.

Many involuntary muscles are constantly at work inside our bodies. The stomach and intestines contract and relax to aid digestion and to move food material along the digestive track. Arteries contract and relax to help move the blood to various parts of the body. These processes take place regardless of any conscious effort on our part.

Not all people have equal control of voluntary muscles. Differences are evident when considering handicaps, such as palsy, which have a wide range of effects on muscular control. It should also be pointed out that even among those not considered handicapped, there are great differences in the ability to control the muscles. This is, in part, responsible for varying abilities in art, athletics, and many other skills.

INTEGRATING: Social studies, physical education

SKILLS: Observing, inferring, classifying, communicating, comparing and contrasting, using space-time relationships, formulating hypotheses

Activity 11.11
WHAT IS MUSCLE SENSE?

Materials Needed

- Blindfold

Procedure

1. Blindfold your partner.

2. Place your partner's left arm in a raised position and ask him or her to hold it there. Then instruct your partner to put the right arm in the same position as the left.

3. Was your partner able to match the position of the left arm with that of the right arm?

4. Move your partner's left arm to a different position and again ask him or her to put the right arm in the same position.

5. Repeat this process several times, sometimes positioning the right arm and asking your partner to match its position with the left arm.

6. Is your partner able to match the position of one arm with the other each time without looking? Why do you think this is so?

7. Trade places. You wear the blindfold and have your partner test your ability to match the position of one arm with the other.

Teacher Information

Certain nerves leading from the muscles to the brain tell the position of the muscles. This is called muscle sense. As a result of muscle sense, people have automatic knowledge of the position of the muscles.

INTEGRATING: Physical education

SKILLS: Observing, communicating

Activity 11.12
HOW FAST DO YOUR NAILS GROW?

Materials Needed

- Nail polish
- Ruler
- Paper and pencil

Procedure

1. Put a tiny spot of nail polish next to the cuticles of one fingernail and one toenail. Let it dry. Plan to leave it there for several weeks.

2. Check the nail polish each day. If it begins to wear away, put another spot of polish on, but be sure to put the new spot exactly on top of the old.

3. Each week, measure the distance from the cuticle to the spot of polish and record it. Do this until the spot of polish grows out to the point that you cut it off when you clip your nails.

4. What was the average weekly growth of your fingernail? Your toenail?

5. Did either your fingernail or toenail grow faster than the other? If so, which one, and how much faster?

For Problem Solvers: Prepare a graph on which all class members can plot their fingernail growth and toenail growth. Then determine what the average fingernail growth is for the class. Compute the average toenail growth also. Do fingernails and toenails grow at the same rate? Is there a difference in nail growth rate between males and females?

Do you think fingernails and toenails grow at the same rate for all ages of people? How could you find out?

Do you think the rate of nail growth could be hereditary? Can you find out?

Teacher Information

A line could be scratched into the nail with a nail file and the polish applied on the scratch. This will increase the life of the polish on the nail and help to assure accurate replacement if it does wear off.

If several students are involved in this activity, some of your problem solvers will enjoy compiling the results and making a graph. If one person or group makes the graph, each student could plot his or her own results. From the group results, with or without the graph, average fingernail and toenail growth rates could be computed for the class. Perhaps some could carry the research a bit further and include other members of their family, thus finding out whether age seems to be a factor in nail growth rate. Comparing results between families will provide indicators of heredity as a factor.

Fingernails normally grow about three times as fast as toenails.

INTEGRATING: Math, social studies

SKILLS: Observing, inferring, classifying, measuring, predicting, communicating, comparing and contrasting, using space-time relationships, formulating hypotheses, identifying and controlling variables, experimenting, researching

Topic 12: The Five Senses

TO THE TEACHER

The human body is a topic of interest, curiosity, and importance to all ages. Formal study of it should begin in the elementary grades. Many things can be done at this early age to increase awareness of the capacities and needs of this marvelous system. As awareness increases, so do appreciation and the ability to care for our bodies properly.

Everything we do involves one or more of the five senses. All that we learn is learned through the senses. Getting acquainted with their bodies is a logical topic for young learners. Scores of activities can be undertaken that involve concrete, firsthand experiences. Many concepts have been encountered before, but new insights and awarenesses should be acquired as those concepts are spotlighted and discussed.

A study of the five senses should include recognition of the handicapped. Those who have lost part, or all, of one or more senses deserve to be recognized and respected as normal human beings. Children should develop an attitude of appreciation for their capabilities without perceiving the handicapped as something less. Indeed, people with full capability of the senses can learn a great deal from those with some degree of loss of hearing, sight, or other capabilities. Frequently, other senses have compensated by becoming sharper and stronger through use, resulting in enhanced awareness.

Activity 12.1
HOW WELL CAN YOU JUDGE DEPTH WITH ONE EYE?

 Take home and do with family and friends.

Materials Needed

- Ping-Pong ball
- Soda bottle
- Table (lower than waist high)

Procedure

1. Stand the soda bottle on the table, about 15 cm (6 in.) from the edge.
2. Place the Ping-Pong ball in the top of the bottle.
3. Walk away at least 3 meters (10 ft.).
4. Face the bottle, cover one eye with your left hand, and walk toward the bottle.
5. As you pass the bottle, try to flip the ball with your finger. Flip only one time and do not pause to flip.
6. What happened?
7. Try it again, covering the other eye.
8. Were the results any different?
9. Try it a third time, leaving both eyes uncovered.
10. What happened this time? Compare the three attempts and explain as best you can.
11. Have someone else try flipping the ball, using the same procedures. Compare the results with your own.

For Problem Solvers: How do you think the use of two eyes makes our judgment of depth and distance more accurate than by using only one eye? Write your hypothesis, then research the question and find out if your hypothesis was right.

Learn about *triangulation* and how distances can be determined by this technique. You might want to talk to someone who knows something about surveying. Share your information with the class.

Teacher Information

In this activity, students will learn that having two eyes serves more of a purpose than simply providing a spare. Accurate depth and distance perception requires two eyes, each of

221

which see objects from a slightly different angle. It is usually difficult to flip the Ping-Pong ball with one eye covered. Students might enjoy practicing to see if they can increase their skill. You might also have them chart the results of several attempts and find out if their accuracy is any greater with one eye than with the other.

INTEGRATING: Reading, language arts, math

SKILLS: Observing, inferring, measuring, communicating, comparing and contrasting, using space-time relationships, formulating hypotheses, identifying and controlling variables, experimenting, researching

Activity 12.2
WHY DO WE NEED FIVE SENSES?

Materials Needed

- Five blindfolds
- Five sheets of paper
- Five pencils
- Chart paper and marker
- Five baby food jars, each containing one of the following: Salt, sand, granulated sugar, powdered sugar, and cornstarch

Procedure

1. Choose five volunteers. Be sure they have not seen the jars containing the five substances.
2. Seat the volunteers at a table and blindfold them.
3. Place one of the jars in front of each volunteer. Also give each one a paper and pencil.
4. Ask each person to feel the contents of the jar and write on the paper what he or she thinks it is. The volunteers are not to taste it, and they are not to say aloud what they think it is.
5. Record the written responses on a chart.
6. Rotate the jars one position to the right.
7. Again have the volunteers feel the contents and write down what they think the substance is. Record the results on the chart.
8. Continue until each of the volunteers has identified all five substances using only the sense of touch.
9. Be sure the chart is where it will not be seen by the volunteers and remove the blindfolds.
10. Place the jars in front of the volunteers in a different order from that of step 3.
11. Ask each volunteer to look at the substance in the jar and write what he or she thinks it is. The volunteers are not to taste or feel the substance. They are not to give their answers aloud, and they must not look at one another's responses.
12. Again rotate the jars, recording the responses of each participant.
13. When all five substances have been identified by all five participants by both touch and sight, let them use other ways to identify the substances. If they suggest tasting, assure them that none of these substances is harmful to taste.
14. Discuss the results. How accurate were the responses from the sense of touch alone? From the sense of sight alone? From a combination of these, and possibly with help from the sense of taste?

15. How do the senses depend on one another? How do all five senses help us to know what is happening around us?

Teacher Information

This activity should emphasize that the senses are interdependent. Discuss the fact that everything we learn is learned through the use of the five senses—frequently a combination of two or more of them. Also discuss how we rely on what we have already learned—information stored in the brain. We acquire certain information about these substances, for instance, by looking, touching, and tasting, but it is only from previous experience that we decide whether it is sugar, salt, or sand.

SKILLS: Observing, inferring, classifying, predicting, communicating, comparing and contrasting

Activity 12.3
HOW CAN YOU SEE THROUGH A SOLID OBJECT?

 Take home and do with family and friends.

Materials Needed

- Cardboard tube, such as a toilet-tissue tube or paper-towel tube
- Book

Procedure

1. Look through the cardboard tube at an object across the room. Keep your other eye open, too.

2. While staring at the object with both eyes, bring your open hand (or a book) against the side of the tube near the far end so the eye not looking through the tube is blocked from seeing the object (remember to keep both eyes open).

3. What happened? Discuss this with your teacher.

Student Looking Through Cardboard Tube

Teacher Information

Your hand or the book, when brought against the side of the tube, will appear to have a hole in it. You will see the object farther away through the hole. Those of us who are fortunate enough to have two eyes have two receptors sending images to the brain simultaneously. The brain combines the two images and the distant object seems to be seen through a hole in your hand.

SKILLS: Observing, communicating

Activity 12.4
HOW FAST DO ODORS TRAVEL?

Materials Needed

- Bowl or saucer
- Perfume or after-shave lotion
- Timer or clock with second hand

Procedure

1. Have the students on one side of the room put their heads down and close their eyes.
2. At the front of the room, put a few drops of the perfume in the bowl and ask the students with their heads down to raise their hands when they smell the perfume. They are not to open their eyes until told to do so.
3. Record the number of seconds it takes for the aroma to reach the first row, second row, third row, and so on.
4. When you are finished, have the students open their eyes.
5. Discuss with the class the results of the investigation.

Teacher Information

This activity will show not only the speed with which aromas move through the air, but the differences in sensitivity of the sense of smell from one person to another. Students might wish to test and compare different perfume brands and fragrances. If so, the bowl will need to be rinsed and the room aired out between trials.

Use the other half of the class to repeat the activity, adding plain water as a secret brand of perfume. Find out how many students "smell" perfume just because they think it's there.

SKILLS: Observing, inferring, using space-time relationships, formulating hypotheses

Activity 12.5
HOW LONG CAN YOU RETAIN A SMELL?

Materials Needed

- Slice of orange
- Blindfold

Procedure

1. Find a partner to do this activity with you.
2. Hold the slice of orange under your partner's nose.
3. Tell your partner to close his or her eyes and to tell when you move the orange slice away.
4. Leave the orange slice under your partner's nose for two minutes, or until he or she reports that it has been removed.
5. What happened? Try to explain why.
6. Try the same activity with other people and with substances other than the orange slice.

For Problem Solvers: Prepare a graph that shows the duration of smell in seconds. Plot on your graph the results from several people, and perhaps with several foods. Compare and discuss the results.

Teacher Information

Other items can be substituted for the orange slice, but each one should have a distinct odor and the odor should not be too strong. The odor-sensitive nerves seem to become accustomed to a given smell in a short time and cease to recognize that odor. The person smelling the orange slice or other substance will usually report in a short time that the item has been removed even though it is still there.

This is a good time to develop or practice graphing skills. Have students make a graph showing smell duration of several people, using the same substance. Other graphs could be made using a variety of substances with the same person.

INTEGRATING: Language arts

SKILLS: Observing, inferring, classifying, measuring, communicating, comparing and contrasting, using space-time relationships, identifying and controlling variables, experimenting

Activity 12.6
WHAT FOODS CAN YOUR NOSE IDENTIFY?

Materials Needed

- Variety of food samples
- Paper cup for each sample
- Toothpicks
- Blindfold
- Markers
- Chart paper

Procedure

1. Choose a partner to help you with this activity.
2. Blindfold your partner.
3. Select one of the food samples and use a toothpick to hold it under your partner's nose for a few seconds. Ask him or her to identify the food.
4. Record your partner's response and indicate whether the food sample was identified accurately.
5. Follow the same procedure for the remaining food samples. For any food sample your partner did not identify correctly, use a toothpick and place a small amount on your partner's tongue. Then see if he or she can tell what the food is.
6. Trade places and ask your partner to give you the same food identification test.
7. Examine the charted results and compare your chart with your partner's chart. Which foods did his or her nose identify correctly without help? Which did yours? Were there any differences? If so, what ideas do you have about the reasons?

For Problem Solvers: With your partner blindfolded, hold a piece of apple under his or her nose while you place a piece of potato in the mouth. With the apple still under the nose, ask your partner to identify the food being eaten.

Can you find other foods of similar texture? If so, try them, too.

Teacher Information

This activity will be more revealing if food samples with varying strength of odors are selected. Students will find that some people can smell certain odors better than others, and that the nose relies, at times, on assistance from the tongue. The nose returns the favor, however, and the sense of taste is often assisted or enhanced by the sense of smell.

SKILLS: Observing, inferring, classifying, predicting, communicating, comparing and contrasting, formulating hypotheses, identifying and controlling variables, experimenting

Activity 12.7
WHAT SOUNDS DO YOU HEAR IN PAPER?

Materials Needed

- Sheets of paper

Procedure

1. Have all your students put their heads down and close their eyes.
2. Make sounds with the paper and have the group try to guess what you are doing with the paper to make each sound. For instance, fold it, cut it, tear it, crumple it up, shake it, drop it on the floor, smooth out the crumpled paper, blow on it.

Teacher Information

This activity lets students use their sense of hearing and their experience with the sounds that can be made with paper. Students might want to take turns making one sound at a time to see if the others can determine what is happening to the paper using the sense of hearing alone. Have them try different kinds of paper, such as ditto paper and construction paper. See if the group can tell what kind of paper is being used as well as what is being done with it.

SKILLS: Observing, inferring

Activity 12.8
HOW WELL DO YOU KNOW YOUR CLASSMATES' VOICES?

Materials Needed

- Blindfold
- Chair

Procedure

1. Do this activity with a group of classmates.
2. Place a chair at the front of the room.
3. Select a volunteer to sit on the chair. This is person 1.
4. Blindfold person 1.
5. Choose a person (person 2) to come up and stand behind person 1.
6. Person 2 knocks on the back of the chair person 1 is sitting in.
7. Person 1 asks, "Who is knocking?"
8. Person 2 answers, "It is I," with a disguised voice.
9. Person 1 has three chances to guess who answered, "It is I."
10. If the guesses are all wrong, another person is selected to be person 2. If the guess is right, person 2 becomes person 1, sits on the chair, and is blindfolded. Another person is selected to come up and knock on the chair.

Teacher Information

This is an exercise in using the sense of hearing, coupled with familiarity with the voices of classmates. The student in the role of person 2 needs to come up to the front of the room very quietly so person 1 doesn't know what part of the room he or she came from. The challenge is in trying to determine whose voice is being disguised.

INTEGRATING: Language arts

SKILLS: Observing, inferring, comparing and contrasting

Activity 12.9
HOW WELL CAN YOUR EARS ALONE TELL YOU WHAT'S HAPPENING?

Materials Needed

- Paper and pencils
- Carrot and grater
- Chalkboard and chalk
- Other optional props

Procedure

1. Do this activity with several partners.
2. Ask the other participants to close their eyes and put their heads down.
3. Instruct them that they are to listen and try to decide what you are doing by using only their ears. They may raise their hands when they think they know.
4. Walk across the floor and see who guesses first what you are doing.
5. Write on the chalkboard.
6. Grate a carrot.
7. Open a drawer.
8. Do a variety of other things and see if the others can tell what you are doing.
9. Make a list of the things the others could identify by using only their ears and a list of things you did that they could not identify.
10. Examine your two lists and discuss reasons you think some of your actions were easier or more difficult for other people to identify by listening.

Teacher Information

Because of our familiarity with some sounds, certain ones are easily recognized. Some are less obvious to us because we don't hear them very much or because they are similar to other sounds we know. This activity should emphasize to students that, although we often need the help of our eyes and other senses, our ears alone frequently provide us with rather accurate information.

You might want to discuss with the class how certain senses become more keen through added use, when others are lost or weakened. The blind, for instance, learn to rely more on their ears, and they notice sounds that the rest of us sometimes do not.

SKILLS: Observing, inferring, communicating, comparing and contrasting

Activity 12.10
HOW MUCH CAN YOU "SEE" WITH YOUR EARS?

Materials Needed

- Curtain or other opaque barrier
- A "sound" skit
- Props (optional)

Procedure

1. Find two or three partners to do this activity with you.
2. Create a short skit, such as a trip to the grocery store, going swimming, or mountain climbing. Your skit is to be heard only, not seen, so write the speaking parts and include any sound effects that might help.
3. Behind the curtain, perform your skit for your class.
4. Tell the class that after your skit is finished you'd like them to describe the events of the play. The class members are to use only their sense of hearing, as all actions are hidden from view.
5. Perhaps other groups in the class would like to try producing a "sound skit."

Teacher Information

Usually, skits are both seen and heard, so we use two senses in getting the meaning of the play. In this activity, students are to use only their sense of hearing. Encourage them to close their eyes as they "observe" with their ears and try to visualize the scenes being acted out in sound.

INTEGRATING: Language arts

SKILLS: Observing, inferring, communicating

Activity 12.11
WHAT IS A STETHOSCOPE?

(Teacher-supervised partners or small groups)

Materials Needed

- Stethoscopes (at least for each two or three participants)
- Soft facial tissue or toilet paper

Procedure

1. Stethoscopes are delicate instruments specially designed to help us listen to functions inside the body. Examine your stethoscope. Notice that it resembles the letter "Y."

2. Can you find the two small rounded ends, held together with a spring? They fit in your ears.

3. Use a soft tissue to clean the rounded ends and carefully put one in each ear. The spring should keep the ends in place. Be sure to clean the ends before each use.

4. Notice that the two hollow tubes coming from the ends in your ears join together to make a single tube.

5. The single tube is attached to a large, flat disc. Carefully examine the flat disc. It has a sensitive vibrator or *diaphragm* that magnifies sound.

6. Put the disc against the part of your body where you think your heart is.

7. Use the stethoscope to listen to other parts inside your body: stomach, throat (try swallowing), lungs (breathe deeply and listen both front and back). Try other places.

8. A stethoscope helps our hearing in the same way hand lenses help our vision. Can you explain how?

For Problem Solvers: Did you know that mechanics sometimes use stethoscopes? What do you suppose the mechanic would use it for? Does a car have a heartbeat? Visit a mechanic and ask to see his or her stethoscope, and ask them to explain how and why they use it. Make a drawing of it and compare it with the medical stethoscope. Share your information with your group, and discuss your ideas about it. Can you think of any other purpose a stethoscope might be useful for?

Teacher Information

With younger children, demonstrate first. Stethoscopes are available from medical personnel—doctors, nurses, dentists, and medical technicians. Some students may have them in their homes. The diaphragms are delicate and should be handled with care.

Some students are familiar with stethoscopes, but many are not. Students can hear many of the normal functions in their own bodies and may be surprised at the normal sounds (such as those in the intestinal tract) that go on regularly inside them. Listening to throats, hearts, and breathing may require partners or teams. Modesty should be observed.

Stethoscopes can also be used to hear the small sounds around us (for example, small insect noises). If possible, have one available at all times for students to use.

Modern technology may make the stethoscope obsolete. Electronic devices are gradually replacing it in many fields of medicine.

INTEGRATING: Physical education

SKILLS: Observing, inferring, classifying, measuring, communicating, researching

Activity 12.12
WHAT DIFFERENCES IN TASTE DO PEOPLE HAVE?

Materials Needed

- Variety of food samples in small pieces
- Paper cups (one for each type of food)
- Box of toothpicks
- Blindfold
- Markers
- Chart paper

Procedure

1. Find a partner to help you with this activity.
2. Blindfold your partner.
3. Using a toothpick, place a small amount of one type of food in the center of your partner's tongue.
4. Have your partner close his or her mouth and move the tongue around for a thorough taste of the sample. Then describe the food as sweet, sour, salty, or bitter. Record the results on a chart something like this:

Name of taster: _____

FOOD	TASTE			
_____	Sweet	Sour	Salty	Bitter

5. Follow the same procedure for each of the food samples, using a new toothpick for each food. The person tasting should rinse his or her mouth with water between food samples. Place the food in the center of the tongue each time.
6. After your partner has tasted all the food samples, trade places and have your partner put the food samples on your tongue. Put the food in the center of the tongue each time and use a new toothpick for each type of food. Your partner should record your judgment of each food type as sweet, sour, salty, or bitter.

Teacher Information

Tastes are usually described as sweet, sour, salty, or bitter. These tastes are strong in some foods and weak in others. Some foods even have combinations of tastes. The purpose of this activity is to compare taste judgments of different people. The different taste-sensitive areas of the tongue are compared in Activity 12.13, and should not become a factor in the above activity; for consistency it is important that each food sample be placed at the center of the tongue.

INTEGRATING: Language arts

SKILLS: Observing, inferring, classifying, communicating, comparing and contrasting, identifying and controlling variables

Activity 12.13
WHICH PART OF THE TONGUE IS MOST SENSITIVE TO TASTE?

Materials Needed

- Variety of food samples
- Paper cups (one for each type of food)
- Box of toothpicks
- Blindfold
- Water
- Chart paper
- Markers

Procedure

1. Find a partner to do this activity with you.

2. Blindfold your partner.

3. Using a toothpick, place a small amount of one type of food on the region of the tongue identified as "1" in the illustration. Your partner is to judge the taste with his or her mouth still open so the food sample is not spread to other regions of the tongue. The taste judgment this time is to indicate strength as well as type of taste: strong sweet, weak sweet, strong salty, weak salty, strong sour, weak sour, strong bitter, or weak bitter.

4. Record your partner's judgment of taste, have him or her rinse the mouth with water, then place the same type of food on region 2, then 3, then 4, then 5. Record the taste judgment each time. Be sure the mouth is rinsed with water between tastes.

5. When you have placed the first food type on all five regions of the tongue and recorded your partner's judgment of taste, do the same with the next food type.

6. After recording your partner's taste judgment of each type of food, trade places and have your partner give you the same taste tests.

7. Analyze the information you have collected in this activity and see if some regions of the tongue seem to be more sensitive to certain tastes than other regions. Make a chart showing your findings.

Teacher Information

Certain regions of the tongue are known to be more sensitive to certain tastes. These are shown in Figure 12.13-2. Results of the above investigations should approximate this information. Have students share and compare their findings. Where differences are found, encourage students to try to identify reasons for the differences. Possible factors include not placing the food sample in the exact same locations, closing the mouth, or spreading the food sample to other parts of the tongue. Also consider differences in taste sensitivities from one person to another (refer to Activity 12.12), or simply the subjectivity of the judgment.

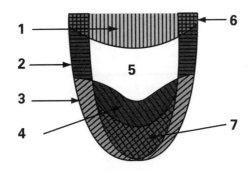

Figure 12.13-1

Taste Regions of the Tongue

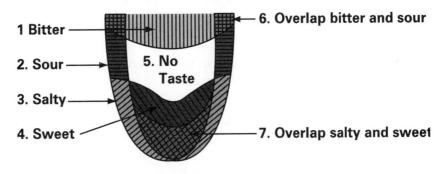

1 Bitter

2. Sour

3. Salty

4. Sweet

5. No Taste

6. Overlap bitter and sour

7. Overlap salty and sweet

Figure 12.13-2

Taste Regions of the Tongue, Labeled

INTEGRATING: Language arts

SKILLS: Observing, inferring, classifying, communicating, comparing and contrasting, identifying and controlling variables

Activity 12.14
HOW CAN WE CLASSIFY FOODS BY TASTE?

Materials Needed

- Variety of foods
- Chart paper
- Markers

Procedure

1. For a period of one day, keep a list of all the food items you eat.
2. As you eat something, think about ways you could describe its taste.
3. As you write each item in your list, write a description of its taste. A word or two is usually sufficient.
4. When you have finished your list, look it over and find foods that in some way have similar taste. Group these together.
5. Compare your list with those of others. Does someone else have some of the same foods? Did they describe the taste the same way you did? Talk together about it.

Teacher Information

If students cannot think of ways to describe taste in order to classify the foods they eat, suggest or discuss the terms normally used to describe taste: sweet, sour, salty, and bitter.

A fun way to do the above activity is to have a party to which each member of the group contributes one food item. Then before anything is eaten have students list all food items involved and classify each one as either sweet, sour, salty, or bitter. They could work individually, in small groups, or as a whole class.

INTEGRATING: Language arts

SKILLS: Observing, inferring, classifying, predicting, communicating, researching

Activity 12.15
HOW DOES A SUDDEN CHANGE IN TEMPERATURE AFFECT US?

Materials Needed

- Large pan or bowl filled with hot water (not hot enough to burn the skin)
- Large pan or bowl filled with warm water
- Large pan or bowl filled with cold water

Procedure

1. Observe the three pans. One has hot water in it, one has warm water in it, and one has cold water in it.
2. *Carefully* put one hand in the hot water and one in the cold. Leave them there for 30 seconds.
3. Now put both hands in the warm water.
4. What happened? What can you say about this?

Teacher Information

When placed in the warm water, the hand that was in the hot water will feel cool while the hand from the cold water will feel warm. A simple explanation for elementary children is that our body has a control system to help us adjust to hot and cold. After one hand has adjusted to hot water and the other has adjusted to cold water, the warm water will feel quite cool to the one and quite warm to the other. This happens because of contrast with that to which they have become accustomed. This is the reason a room feels hot when we first come in from the cold outdoors or vice versa.

SKILLS: Observing, inferring, measuring, communicating, comparing and contrasting, identifying and controlling variables

Activity 12.16
WHERE IS YOUR SENSE OF TOUCH MOST SENSITIVE?

Materials Needed

- None

Procedure

1. Do this activity with a partner.

2. Ask your partner to close his or her eyes.

3. Place the tips of three of your fingers, about 3 cm (1 in.) apart on your partner's back. Ask your partner to tell you how many fingers are touching.

4. Touch the palm of your partner's hand with one finger, then two. See if your partner can tell without looking how many fingers you are using.

5. Do the same on the shoulder, the forearm, the neck, the forehead, and the back.

6. In what areas is your partner able to tell with the most accuracy how many fingers you are using?

7. Trade places and have your partner test your sense of touch in the same manner.

8. Compare the results. Is your sense of touch the most sensitive in the same areas as that of your partner?

For Problem Solvers: Draw an outline of the human body and identify areas of greater or lesser sensitivity. Use a 1, 2, 3 rating. First, mark the outline with your predicted ratings, then test the areas of the body and mark the areas again, showing your findings with a different color of ink. Compare your information with that of others who are doing the activity.

Teacher Information

Sometimes it is surprising to find out how little sensitivity we have on some parts of the body. Students usually find that on their hands, fingers, and face they can tell quite accurately how many fingers are touching. On the back and arms the sense of touch is noticeably less sensitive. They might like to discuss times when they have noticed that injuries are much more painful in some places than in others.

INTEGRATING: Physical education

SKILLS: Observing, inferring, classifying, predicting, communicating, comparing and contrasting, formulating hypotheses, identifying and controlling variables

Activity 12.17
WHAT PARTS OF YOUR BODY CAN FEEL THINGS BEST?

Materials Needed

- Blindfold
- Variety of objects, such as a ball, a pencil, a book, an eraser, a piece of crumpled paper

Procedure

1. Find a partner to help you with this activity.
2. Blindfold your partner.
3. Select one of the objects and place it on the table in front of your partner.
4. Tell your partner that he or she is to identify the object on the table by feeling it, but the hands are not to be used. The arms, face, feet, or anything but the hands may be used.
5. Have someone else try the same thing, but with a different object to identify.
6. Discuss the experience. Was it easy? What part of the body did you want to use? What parts of the body have the greatest sense of touch?

Teacher Information

The children should note that the sense of touch is the only one of the five senses that is not confined to the head area. The organ of the body that is usually associated with the sense of touch is the skin, although areas inside the body have varying amounts of touch sensitivity as well.

Not all areas of the skin have the same degree of sensitivity to touch. One of the areas of greater sensitivity is the fingertips. Because of this and the dexterity of the fingers, we usually use our fingers to feel something. This activity should help participants realize why we use our fingers to do this and how little sensitivity some of the other parts of the body have.

If you have been using a "feely box" for activities with the sense of touch, items from it would be excellent to use in the above activity. These are items the children have already experienced with the fingers, and they will be able to compare the task of identifying them with other parts of the body.

SKILLS: Observing, communicating, comparing and contrasting, identifying and controlling variables

Activity 12.18
WHAT IS WARM AND WHAT IS COLD?

Materials Needed

- Three pans or bowls
- Hot, lukewarm, and cold water
- Blindfold

Procedure

1. Find another student to do this activity with you.
2. Fill one pan with cold water, one with lukewarm water, and one with hot water. The hot water must not be hot enough to burn or hurt.
3. Blindfold your partner.
4. Have your partner put the left hand in the hot water and then put the right hand in the lukewarm water.
5. Ask your partner to describe the temperature of the water in the two bowls.
6. Have your partner remove both hands from the water.
7. Shift the bowls around, then have your partner put the left hand in the cold water and the right hand in the lukewarm water.
8. Ask your partner to again describe the temperature of the water in the two bowls.
9. Think about the result. Did your partner describe the lukewarm water as lukewarm both times? Did his or her judgment of the lukewarm bowl seem to be affected by the temperature of the water the other hand was in? How was it affected? What can you say about this?
10. Try the same activity with another person and see if you get the same result.

Teacher Information

When we say something is hot or cold, we are usually thinking in terms of its comparison to something else. Boiling water isn't very hot compared with molten steel, for instance. We sometimes get a glass of water from the cold-water tap and complain about the water being warm, but if we were to take a shower in water of the same temperature we would probably consider it very cold. This activity is designed to point out that our reactions to temperatures are relative. We frequently judge something to be hot or cold relative to the temperature of the skin. The lukewarm water used in this activity should be such that it feels neither hot nor cold to the skin. When the blindfolded person puts one hand into it after the other hand is already in hot water, however, the lukewarm water will probably be described as cold or cool because of the contrast with the hot water. To the hand that has been in cold water, the lukewarm water will feel warm.

SKILLS: Observing, inferring, communicating, comparing and contrasting, identifying and controlling variables

Activity 12.19
HOW MANY TOUCH WORDS CAN YOU FIND?

Materials Needed

- Paper
- Pencils
- Bowl or small box

Procedure

1. Do this activity with a group of your classmates.
2. Write a touch word (such as hard, soft, smooth, rough) on each of several small pieces of paper. The words used should describe objects that are in the room or otherwise accessible.
3. Fold the papers and put them in the bowl.
4. Divide the participants into two teams.
5. Draw a paper from the bowl and read the word.
6. Each team should find something that will match the word that is read. The first team to find an item to match the touch word gets a point.
7. Draw another paper. Repeat the process until the time is up or a predetermined number of points is reached.

Teacher Information

This activity gives students an opportunity to use many descriptive words that are associated with the sense of touch and to match those words with objects they describe. Here is a beginning list of touch words you or your students can choose from in making the papers to go in the bowl:

Hard	Heavy	Smooth	Soft	Solid	Wet
Dry	Spongy	Hairy	Dusty	Stiff	Scratchy
Rough	Hot	Cold	Lukewarm	Slippery	Silky
Sticky	Bumpy	Lumpy	Bristly	Coarse	Woolly
Furry	Oily	Prickly	Limp	Gooey	Greasy
Gritty	Flabby	Fluffy	Fuzzy	Slimy	Squishy
Thorny	Stretchable	Springy	Slick	Cuddly	

As a follow-up activity, consider having the children think of some touch experiences that are sometimes associated with emotions or feelings. Have them describe touch experiences that make them feel warm, cold, itchy, tingly, frightened, excited, safe, happy, eerie, and so forth.

INTEGRATING: Language arts

SKILLS: Observing, inferring, classifying, communicating

Topic 13:   Health and Nutrition

TO THE TEACHER

Every person needs to develop wise eating habits and understand some basic concepts and principles for proper care of the body. Some children have access to little food and need to be especially careful that what they eat is nutritious. Many have excessive amounts of junk food available to them and considerable social pressure or desire to consume unhealthful amounts of it. The activities of this section will help to increase awareness of good eating habits, proper hygiene, and care of the teeth.

Someone said commitment comes partly through ownership of an idea. This is a good time to get students involved in researching, writing, and sharing reports on topics related to the activities herein, and in teaching one another. The process of teaching someone else good health habits will increase the level of commitment, on the part of the presenters, to develop those habits themselves.

Activity 13.1
WHAT ARE WE MADE OF?

(Teacher demonstration in a sink, large bucket, or dishpan)

Materials Needed

- Small 20–40 liter (5–10 gallon) *opaque* garbage bag
- Water
- Food products in small quantities such as hard-boiled egg; milk; green, leafy vegetables; yellow vegetables (squash); piece of whole-wheat bread; soy or any dry beans; potato with skin left on; small pieces of fruit—orange, apple, etc.; nuts
- Slice of pizza (avoid fresh meat and fish)
- Flashlight battery
- Tablespoon of salt
- Pinch of dirt

Procedure

1. Add water to the bag until it is about three fourths full.
2. As you add small quantities of the other materials in the list, discuss the importance (to human health and nutrition) of each item.
3. Continue to add items (especially leafy vegetables and fruit) until the bag is full.
4. Seal the top of the bag. Carefully shake the contents.
5. Although the amounts are not in proportion, this bag is the way a chemist might see us. In order to grow, we must continue to add water and nutritional foods to our bag.

Teacher Information

You can keep costs down by using small quantities and perhaps asking your produce department at the local grocery store for scraps.

This simple idea may help introduce the following concepts:

a. Our body is mostly water.
b. Various foods contain different amounts of elements our body must have.
c. A balanced diet means giving our bodies the right kinds and quantities of many foods.
d. One important purpose of our skin is to prevent harmful things from entering the body. In our model, the garbage bag represents the skin, which is the largest organ of the body.

The salt and dirt represent bacteria and compounds that are natural and essential to body functions. You may want to discuss health problems that require limitations in salt and other substances and the difference between harmful and helpful bacteria in the human body.

The flashlight battery is optional and probably should be used only with older students, although younger ones may relate to the concept of energy in the body. It represents the chemical reactions that produce electrical energy from which our brain and nervous system operate.

Life processes such as digestion, respiration, and elimination are not included in this simple model. However, the model could trigger many creative and challenging questions, such as: "Now that we have all the necessary chemical contents in this bag, why isn't it alive?" or "What does your body do that this bag cannot?"

SKILLS: Observing, inferring, classifying, measuring, communicating, using space-time relationships, identifying and controlling variables

Activity 13.2
WHY ARE THE BASIC FOOD GROUPS IMPORTANT?

Materials Needed

- Paper and pencil
- Encyclopedia
- Health books
- Other books about food
- Small group of students

Procedure

1. With your class or group, select one of the following basic food groups to study:

   a. Vegetables and fruits

   b. Meat

   c. Bread and cereals

   d. Milk and milk products

2. Search the reference books you have for answers to the following questions regarding your food group:

   a. What do these foods have in common?

   b. What do these foods do for our bodies?

   c. What vitamins and minerals do these foods provide?

   d. How many calories are usually in a normal serving?

   e. Are these foods expensive?

3. Report your findings to the class.

For Problem Solvers: Arrange to interview a nurse or other nutrition expert. Prepare your questions in advance. Use a tape recorder or camcorder to record the interview. Include the recording of this interview as a part of your report.

Ask the nurse or nutrition expert to help you find a magazine article about a group of people who do not get adequate nutrition. Study and prepare a report on this information.

Teacher Information

A balanced diet is necessary for our bodies to have energy to keep warm, to do our work, and to play. Our bodies must also have materials for repair and growth and to keep the organs functioning properly.

This exercise works well as a class activity, with each group of students assigned a different food group to explore. When they have gathered their information, have each group share their findings with the rest of the class. Preparation for these reports provides an excellent opportunity for students to practice their skills at illustrating with pictures and compiling information into charts. With all information in, have students plan a balanced diet, using the information learned in this activity. This could be done either by individuals or in groups, according to the interest and ability of the students.

INTEGRATING: Reading, language arts, social studies

SKILLS: Communicating, formulating hypotheses, identifying and controlling variables, experimenting, researching

Activity 13.3
WHAT ARE THE MOST COMMON AND THE MOST POPULAR FOODS?

Materials Needed

- Copies of the "Food I Like and Food I Eat" activity sheet
- Chart paper
- Pencils
- Marker

Procedure

1. Make several copies of the "Food I Like and Food I Eat" activity sheet and write "Breakfast" at the top of each.
2. Give a copy of this sheet to each of several people and ask them to write the food items they *most commonly eat* for breakfast (at least once each week) in the left column and the foods they *prefer* for breakfast in the right column.
3. Collect the sheets.
4. Write all the food items people included in the left column on a "Common and Popular Foods" chart.
5. For each item in the list, count the number of people who eat that item regularly and write the number in the "How Many Eat" column on the chart.
6. For each item in the list, count the number of people who prefer that item and write that number in the "How Many Prefer" column on the chart.
7. Display the chart on the wall.

For Problem Solvers: Repeat this activity for lunch foods and for dinner foods. Share your information along with the information on breakfast foods.

Teacher Information

This activity could be done by an individual or a committee. A class discussion of the popular and common foods and the reasons we eat what we do could be a valuable follow-up. The discussion should include the relative nutritional value.

While this activity is being conducted, other individuals or groups could be gathering similar information for lunch and dinner foods. Or this could be done by your problem solvers who are motivated to do more after doing their research on breakfast foods.

You might want to have students begin by writing a list of the foods they predict are the most common and popular foods.

INTEGRATING: Reading, math

SKILLS: Communicating, researching

FOOD I LIKE AND FOOD I EAT

Meal: _____

Food I eat most: **Food I like most:**

COMMON AND POPULAR FOODS

Food Item	How Many Eat	How Many Prefer

Food Charts

Activity 13.4
HOW WELL BALANCED IS YOUR DIET?

Materials Needed

- Paper
- Pencils
- Encyclopedia or health text

Procedure

1. Write a "Three-Meal Menu" of everything you eat for breakfast, lunch, and dinner today. Do this for three days.
2. Find a list of the four basic food groups in your encyclopedia or health book.
3. Examine your menus of food you consumed for three days. Beside each food item, write which food group that item belongs to.
4. At the bottom of each "Three-Meal Menu," write the names of the four food groups and the number of items you consumed that day from each group.
5. Do you show a balanced diet (at least one serving from each of the four food groups) for each day? If not, write down which food group(s) you need to include in your diet more frequently.

For Problem Solvers: Collect the results from all students in the class, without names attached, and prepare a chart that shows the frequency of consumption of the food groups by the class. Discuss the results with your class, and emphasize the weak spots you find in the chart—the food groups that are most frequently lacking in the diets of the class members.

Teacher Information

If school lunch is served at your school, be sure to include it as one of the daily meals used for this activity.

Students should easily be able to find, in their health book or encyclopedia, reference to the four basic food groups (fruits and vegetables, breads and cereals, meat, and dairy products). If students have already completed Activity 13.3 and still have their record of food eaten, they could use that information instead of rewriting the food items for nine meals as indicated above.

After students have completed this activity, discuss their findings. They should be cautioned to include frequent servings of each of the four basic food groups in their diet (at least one from each group every day), and to avoid excessive amounts of sugar and of foods that contain a lot of fat, such as ice cream and fatty meat. You might even make a class chart (without names) showing the frequency of consumption of the four food groups. This will spotlight the extent to which the class is getting a balanced diet and which, if any, food groups are being short-changed. This is a good extension for your problem solvers.

INTEGRATING: Language arts

SKILLS: Classifying, communicating, using space-time relationships, researching

PHYSICAL SCIENCE ACTIVITIES

Topics

- **Nature of Matter**
- **Energy**
- **Light**
- **Sound**
- **Simple Machines**
- **Magnetism**
- **Static Electricity**

Topic 14:   Nature of Matter

TO THE TEACHER

Everything around us is matter of one form or another. The air we breathe, the food we eat, the books we read, our bodies——all of these things are made of various types of chemicals and substances. The topic of this section is very broad and is related to many other science topics. No attempt has been made to be comprehensive in coverage, but only to expose students to a few of the basic properties and relationships of matter. Activities have been selected that involve materials and supplies common to the school or the home in preference to those requiring sophisticated equipment.

It is recommended that after a study of the nature of matter, you seek opportunities to apply the general concepts learned while studying other science topics. For example, in a study of weather, air, or water, the principles of evaporation and condensation are essential. The effect of temperature change on expansion and contraction is another idea common to weather, air, water, and the topic of this section. In a study of plants, animals, or the human body, the nature of matter has many applications.

Activity 14.1
WHAT IS THE SHAPE OF A DROP OF WATER?

 Take home and do with family and friends.

Materials Needed

- Waxed paper
- Water
- Eye dropper
- Pencil

Procedure

1. Draw some water into the dropper.

2. Put several drops on the waxed paper, keeping each separate from the others. Hold the dropper about 1 cm (1/2 in.) above the waxed paper as you squeeze lightly on the bulb.

3. Examine the drops of water. What is their shape? How do they compare in size?

4. Put the point of your pencil into a drop of water, observing carefully to see how the water responds. What did the drop of water do at the surface? Do the water molecules seem to be more attracted to the pencil lead or to each other?

5. Push one of the drops around with your pencil point, observing its behavior.

6. Push two drops together—then three or four. What did they do as they came near each other?

7. What can you say about the attraction of water molecules for each other? For the pencil lead? For the waxed paper?

8. If you could put a drop of water out in space where there is no gravity, what do you think it would look like? What shape would it have?

For Problem Solvers: Place a drop of water on various surfaces and examine each drop with a hand lens. Try it on a sheet of plastic, a sheet of paper, and aluminum foil. Try it on a paper towel. What is the shape of the drop of water? What differences do you see?

Place a drop of water on a penny. Now what is its shape? How many more drops do you think you could put on the penny? Write your estimate, then try it and test your estimate.

Teacher Information

Water molecules attract one another. The attraction of like molecules for one another is called *cohesion*. Within the liquid the force of this attraction is balanced, as each molecule is attracted by other molecules all the way around. The molecules on the surface are pulled downward and sideways but not up. This creates a skinlike effect called *surface tension*. The roundness of the drops on the waxed paper is an indication of surface tension. When several drops are put together they flatten out more, because of the increased effect of gravity.

Because of surface tension, a drop of water in the absence of gravity would take on the shape of a perfect sphere. However, a drop of water out in space would evaporate almost instantly.

The surface tension of water forms a bond strong enough to support the weight of a razor blade or paper clip laid carefully on the water. When detergent is added to the water, the surface tension is broken and the floating object will sink.

Many other substances have surface tension. It has been suggested that better ball bearings could be formed in space than in factories on earth because a drop of molten steel would naturally form a perfect sphere.

SKILLS: Observing, inferring, predicting, communicating

Activity 14.2
HOW CAN YOU GET SALT OUT OF PEPPER?

 Take home and do with family and friends.

Materials Needed

- Plastic bag
- 1/2 cup salt
- 1 teaspoon pepper

Procedure

1. Mix the salt and the pepper together in the bag.
2. Now your challenge is to get the pepper out of the salt. How might you do it?
3. Test your ideas.

Teacher Information

This activity is intended to help children learn to conduct and evaluate problem-solving procedures. There is no "right" answer but some procedures may be more effective or efficient than others. For example, picking the pepper out is slow and tedious. Dissolving the salt in water and straining the solution through a cloth is more efficient. Encourage the children to think of and try as many ways as possible. This could introduce a discussion of the way science and technology have combined to find easier and more efficient ways to do things.

SKILLS: Observing, inferring

Activity 14.3
WHAT ARE MIXTURES AND SOLUTIONS?

Materials Needed

- Two glass jars
- Spoons (or stirrers)
- Sugar
- Water
- Marbles or small rocks
- Paper clips
- Toothpicks
- Bits of paper
- Paper and pencil

Procedure

1. Fill each jar about half full of water.
2. Put the marbles, paper clips, toothpicks, and bits of paper in one jar and a spoonful of sugar in the other jar.
3. Stir both jars and observe what happens to the materials in the water.
4. Compare the results in the two jars. One is a mixture and the other is a solution.
5. Try other substances in water, such as sand, powdered milk, or powdered chocolate. Make a list of those you think produce mixtures and those that produce solutions. Explain the differences you observe.

For Problem Solvers: Try to identify mixtures and solutions that are already in your environment. What about the soil in a flower bed at home or at school? What about the air? Make a list of all the mixtures you can find in nature and another list of all the solutions you can find. Notice different food products in your cupboards at home or on grocery-store shelves. Add these to your lists.

Teacher Information

A mixture consists of two or more substances that retain their separate identities when mixed together. Solutions result when the substance placed in a liquid seems to become part of the liquid. A solution is really a special kind of mixture—one in which the particles are all molecular in size.

Materials listed can easily be substituted or supplemented with other soluble and non-soluble materials.

SKILLS: Observing, inferring, classifying, comparing and contrasting

Activity 14.4
IS THE DISSOLVING OF SOLIDS A PHYSICAL CHANGE OR A CHEMICAL CHANGE?

Materials Needed

- Tumbler
- Sugar (or salt)
- Paper and pencil
- Water
- Stirrer

Procedure

1. Put about two teaspoons of sugar and a small amount of water in a tumbler and stir until the sugar is completely dissolved.

2. Put the tumbler where it can remain undisturbed while the water evaporates.

3. Check the tumbler twice each day. If you notice anything different about it, record your observations.

4. When the water has completely evaporated, record your observations of the tumbler. Do you think the dissolving of the sugar in the water was a physical change or a chemical change? Why do you think as you do? Support your answer with your observations.

For Problem Solvers: Take a small piece of paper and tear it up into the smallest bits you can. Was that a physical change or a chemical change? Place a drop of lemon juice on a piece of paper, and let it dry. Is a physical change or a chemical change taking place? Hold the paper near a light bulb until it begins to look different where the drop of juice was. Is this a physical change or a chemical change? Identify other physical changes and chemical changes that occur in your world. What about a cake as it bakes? What about the soles of your shoes, as they slowly wear away?

Teacher Information

A physical change usually alters only the state of matter, such as from a solid to a liquid or from a liquid to a gas, or the shape, texture, etc. Physical changes are frequently reversible. For example, water can be obtained by condensing it out of the air or by melting an ice cube. Chemical changes involve changes in molecular structure and are not reversible. As the water in this activity evaporates, crystals of sugar appear. They will be massed together and will not look the same, but a taste will reveal that it is sugar.

You might also burn a bit of sugar for students to compare. After the burned substance has cooled, let someone taste it and determine whether the sugar underwent a physical change or a chemical change. It will no longer taste like sugar, except to the extent that unburned sugar crystals remain. The burning process produces a chemical change. The sugar has been oxidized through heat, leaving a carbon residue.

INTEGRATING: Math

SKILLS: Observing, inferring, classifying, measuring, comparing and contrasting

Activity 14.5
WHAT IS RUST?

Materials Needed

- Two small identical jars
- Two small identical dishes
- Paper and pencil
- Steel wool
- Water

Procedure

1. Put a small wad of steel wool into one of the jars. Push it clear to the bottom. Pack it just tightly enough that it will stay at the bottom of the jar when the jar is turned upside down.

2. Put about 2 cm (3/4 in.) of water in each of the two dishes. Be sure you put the same amount in each one.

3. Turn the two jars upside down and stand one in each of the dishes. One jar should have steel wool in the bottom and one should be empty.

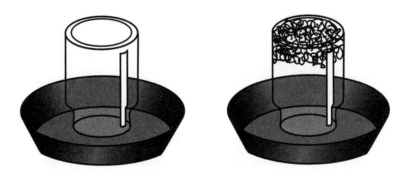

**Two Dishes with Inverted Jars
One Has Steel Wool**

4. Examine the jars each day for one week and record your observations, noting such things as water level and appearance of the steel wool.

5. At the end of one week, study the recorded day-by-day observations and explain the noted changes.

For Problem Solvers: Notice the color of the rust that forms on the steel wool. Try to find items that are made of steel or iron and that have been used for a long time and examine them for spots of rust. See if you can find the same thing on items that are made of plastic. Find out what stainless steel is, then find some items that are made of stainless steel. Can you find rust on them? Look up stainless steel in your encyclopedia and try to find out how stainless steel is different and why it is used.

Teacher Information

As steel wool is exposed to moist air over a period of time, the moisture serves as a medium to bring oxygen molecules in the air in close contact with molecules of iron in the steel wool. Oxygen molecules and iron molecules combine to make iron oxide. This process uses up some of the oxygen in the air inside the jar, reducing the amount of gas (air) in the jar. This, in turn, reduces the air pressure inside the jar, thus the atmospheric pressure outside the jar is greater than the pressure inside the jar, and water is forced into the jar. Student observations should include the rising water level inside the jar containing steel wool as well as the rust color forming on the steel wool.

INTEGRATING: Math, reading

SKILLS: Observing, inferring, comparing and contrasting, measuring

Topic 15:   Energy

TO THE TEACHER

We use many forms of energy every day, yet we never see it. The sun's energy literally powers the earth, but it is so common we take it for granted. It is just there. Energy comes in many forms, none of which looks like "energy." It is disguised as a match stick, a lump of coal, a gallon of gasoline, or a glass of orange juice; it is never just energy. In a broad sense, energy is so much a part of us and our surroundings that it would be impossible to deal with it as a topic separate from other topics treated in this book. The sun's energy keeps us warm and gives us light. Part of the sun's energy is converted by plants into food for animals. Cattle convert some of that energy from plant form to muscle, which we eat (beefsteak, hamburger, and so forth). Energy is consumed by people in both plant and animal form. We, in turn, convert it into human flesh and bones. The sun's energy is a vital ingredient of our own bodies and of a great deal of our surroundings.

In a narrower sense, energy is sometimes defined as the capacity for performing work (*Webster's New Collegiate Dictionary*). It exists in two forms, potential energy and kinetic energy. *Potential energy* is the ability to do work. Work is defined as force acting through a distance. Specifically, Work = Force × Distance. *Kinetic energy* is the energy of motion. A rubber band stretched out has potential energy. When it is released, its potential energy is converted to kinetic energy. A stick of dynamite has potential energy. When a small electrical charge or the right amount of heat is applied, the potential energy is converted to kinetic energy with great force.

The potential energy in dynamite is chemical energy. The potential energy in the rubber band, or in a set mousetrap, or in a raised hammer is mechanical energy.

The energy we consume in the form of meat, fruit, and vegetables isn't all used to build body cells. We use some of it to walk and talk. We even use some of this energy as we think.

Most sections of this book deal directly or indirectly with forms of energy. This section recognizes these but emphasizes additional topics, such as heat, gravity, and the relationship between energy and work.

Activities that appear complex can usually be used in the lower grades by deemphasizing terminology and mathematical applications. With simplified explanations of the concepts, children can participate in the activities and benefit from exposure to these principles.

Activity 15.1
HOW CAN WIND ENERGY BE USED TO TURN SOMETHING?

Materials Needed

- Square poster paper (about 15 cm [6 in.] square)
- Pencil with eraser
- Straight pin
- Scissors
- Ruler
- Stapler

Procedure

1. Draw two lines on the card from corner to corner. The lines should cross at the center.

2. Make a pencil mark at the center of the card, where the lines cross (see Figure 15.1-1).

3. You now have a center point and four lines that connect the center point to the corners of the card.

4. Make a pencil mark on each of the four lines, 2.5 cm (1 in.) from the center point.

5. Make four cuts in the card with the scissors. Cut along each line, from the corner toward the center point, to the mark you made on the line.

6. You now have eight points. Fold every other point into the center of the card.

7. Staple the folded points at the center. This is your windmill.

8. Push the straight pin through the center of the windmill and into the eraser of the pencil (see Figure 15.1-2). Blow on the pinwheel to see that it spins freely.

9. When the wind blows, take your pinwheel outdoors. Share it with others.

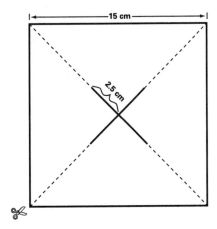

Figure 15.1-1

Card Prepared for the Pinwheel

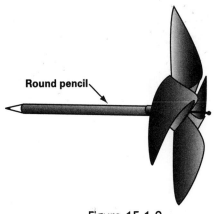

Figure 15.1-2

Pinwheel

For Problem Solvers: Find two plastic or paper drinking cups. One of these can be very small. Push the pencil through the larger cup, so the cup becomes a stand for the pinwheel. Tape one end of the string to the pencil, near the end opposite the pinwheel, and fasten the other end of the string to the small cup (see Figure 15.1-3). Blow on the pinwheel and the string should wind around the pencil, lifting the cup. Now let's call it a *windmill*.

Next, your challenge is to think of other ways to move things with wind power. You might make a different design of windmill or a completely different device. Discuss your ideas with others and learn together.

By the way, where does wind energy come from? Trace its source.

Figure 15.1-3

Windmill Ready to Raise a Load

Teacher Information

In this activity students use wind as a source of energy. Discuss the notion that even wind energy comes from the sun. Challenge students to explain that.

As students create objects that use wind as a source of energy to move something, they develop their creative skills and their problem-solving skills. If your problem solvers get bogged down in trying to think of ideas, you might want to encourage them to first research ways that wind power has been used and is now used. As they learn about ways wind power has been used historically, perhaps new and creative ideas will come to them. Encourage students also to discuss their ideas with one another. Talking about an idea often stimulates new thoughts for the person who is doing the explaining.

INTEGRATING: Reading, language arts, math, social studies

SKILLS: Observing, inferring, measuring, predicting, communicating, identifying and controlling variables, experimenting, researching

Activity 15.2
HOW CAN YOU GET THE MOST HEAT ENERGY FROM THE SUN?

Materials Needed

- Three identical jars
- Paper and pencil
- Black paper
- Aluminum foil
- Tape
- Three thermometers
- Sand

Procedure

1. Fill the three jars with sand.
2. Cover one jar with black paper, including the top, and tape the paper in place.
3. Cover the second jar with aluminum foil, including the top, and tape the foil in place.
4. Leave the third jar uncovered.
5. Record the temperature shown on the thermometers. Be sure all three indicate the same temperature.
6. Insert one thermometer into the sand in each jar. With the two covered jars, puncture a hole in the top covering and insert the thermometer through the hole.
7. Place all three jars in sunlight. All should receive the same direct sunlight.
8. Check and record the temperature of the three thermometers every 15 minutes for about two hours.
9. How do the temperatures compare? What can you say about the effect of a black surface and a shiny surface on absorption of energy from the sun?
10. Remove the jars from the sunlight and continue to record the temperatures of the three thermometers for two more hours.
11. How do the temperature changes compare? What can you say about the effect of a black surface and a shiny surface on heat loss?

For Problem Solvers: Here are more ways to compare the effect of color on heat absorption. Place a thermometer on a paper plate and lay a sheet of black paper over it. Prepare a second plate using a thermometer and white paper, then a third using aluminum foil. On a warm, sunny day, place all three plates in direct sunlight. Check and record the temperatures on the thermometers after one-half hour, then again after one hour.

If you live in a cold climate, place papers of various colors on a snow bank, in the sunlight. Use a black paper, a white paper, and a piece of aluminum foil of the same size. Use other colors also if you'd like to. Line them up, so they all have direct sunlight. After an hour, check the snow under the papers to find out how much has melted. Check them again after two hours.

Share your results with your class.

Teacher Information

The uncovered jar of sand will provide a control to help students observe the effect of both the black and the shiny surface. The temperature of the jar with the black surface will likely increase noticeably faster than that of the other two. The foil will reflect heat and the temperature increase of the sand covered by it will be very slow.

Astronauts wear reflective clothing to help protect them from the direct rays of the sun.

INTEGRATING: Math

SKILLS: Observing, inferring, classifying, measuring, predicting, communicating, comparing and contrasting, using space-time relationships, formulating hypotheses, identifying and controlling variables, experimenting

Activity 15.3
WHAT OTHER TYPE OF ENERGY ACCOMPANIES LIGHT FROM THE SUN?

(Teacher-supervised activity)

Materials Needed

- Two magnifying glasses
- One sheet of paper
- Glass bowl

Procedure

1. Ask your teacher where you should do this experiment. You will need to be in bright sunlight with no wind.
2. Put the paper in the bowl.
3. Hold the magnifying glass between the paper and the sun so a beam of light focuses on the paper.
4. Notice that as you move the magnifying glass closer to and farther from the paper, the point of light changes in size. Notice also that it gets brighter as it gets smaller.
5. Adjust the distance between the paper and the magnifying glass to make the point of light very small and bright.
6. Pull the magnifying glass back about 1 cm (1/2 in.) and watch the paper.
7. Do you see anything happening to the paper? If so what, and why do you think it is happening? What kind of energy is causing this to happen?
8. What do you think might happen if you used two magnifying glasses focused on the same spot on the paper? Try it.

Figure 15.3-1

Magnifying Glass with Sheet of Paper in Glass Bowl

274

Teacher Information

As light rays from the sun are concentrated by a magnifying glass, so are the infrared, or heat, rays. The magnifying glass can concentrate bright sunlight to such a degree that it will scorch the paper or even possibly ignite it. As illustrated in Figure 15.3-2, the focal distance for heat (infrared) rays is slightly longer than the focal distance for light. For this reason, step 5 suggests moving the lens back slightly after the focal point is found. You will need to adjust the distance from lens to paper slightly to find the focal point for heat—the point at which the greatest possible concentration of heat is focused on the paper.

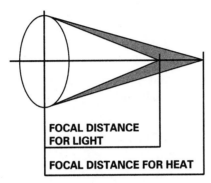

Figure 15.3-2

Focal Distance for Heat and Light

SKILLS: Observing, inferring, classifying, measuring, predicting, communicating, using space-time relationships, formulating hypotheses, identifying and controlling variables, experimenting

275

Activity 15.4
HOW DO MOLECULES BEHAVE WHEN HEATED?

(Teacher demonstration)

Materials Needed

- Chalk or masking tape

Procedure

1. Have several students stand in a group.

2. Mark a border on the floor around the group with chalk or tape. Leave a few inches between the group and the border all the way around.

3. Ask students to move around slowly. Everyone should move constantly, but no one should move fast and there should be no pushing and shoving. They are to try to stay within the border marked on the floor.

4. Now instruct those in the group to move a bit faster. They are still to try to stay within the border.

5. Continue speeding up the movement of the group until they can no longer remain within the line marked on the floor.

6. Discuss what happened as those in the group increased their speed. Ask how this relates to the movement of molecules as temperature is increased.

Teacher Information

As a substance increases in temperature, molecules move faster but do not increase in size. In their rapid movement they bump into each other more frequently and require more space, just as did the group of students. If the members of the group were all running at top speed, they would have required much more space.

INTEGRATING: Physical education

SKILLS: Observing, inferring, comparing and contrasting

Topic 16:   Light

TO THE TEACHER

Like many other scientific phenomena, light is so common that we take it for granted. Yet without it we could not live. Plants use light from the sun to produce oxygen, which is vital to all animal life, including humans. Without plants we would have no food. Light from the sun also heats the earth, and without heat there could be no life at all.

The question of what light really is has evaded scientists for centuries. Yet it is as fascinating as it is elusive, and continues to be the object of many studies. We know a great deal about light because of these studies. For instance, we know that light is a form of energy that travels freely through space. We also know that in addition to the sources of natural light (the sun and the stars), light can be created in various ways. When light comes from sources that people control, it is called artificial light. We use artificial light every day in the form of fluorescent lights and incandescent lights. The laser produces a form of light that has found widespread use in industry, medicine, and communications.

Activities included in this section encourage investigation into some of the ways in which light behaves. As students participate in these activities, the teacher should encourage them to ponder the relationship of this topic to the study of the eyes and to art.

The scope of the activities in this section is limited to a few very basic concepts about light. Students investigate shadows, color, reflection, and refraction, and they are introduced to prisms and lenses. Many of these concrete activities are easily adaptable for children in the early grades. For the student whose interests extend beyond these basic investigations, many resources are available—trade books, encyclopedias, science reference books, and suppliers of scientific equipment.

Activity 16.1
HOW DOES COLOR AFFECT ENERGY ABSORBED FROM LIGHT?

Materials Needed

- Two equally calibrated thermometers
- Heat lamp (or a high-wattage bulb)
- One sheet of white paper and one sheet of black paper of the same thickness
- Paper and pencil

Procedure

1. Prop the thermometers in an upright position about 20 cm (8 in.) apart, facing in the same direction.
2. Record the temperatures of both thermometers.
3. Place the sheet of white paper in front of one thermometer and the black paper in front of the other.
4. Shine the heat lamp at the sheets of paper in such a way that it faces both equally. It should be about 40–50 cm (16–20 in.) away from the papers.
5. After the heat lamp has shone on the papers for about two minutes, check and record the temperatures of the two thermometers again.
6. Repeat for two more minutes and again record the temperatures.
7. Compare the changes in the first and last temperature readings of the two thermometers.
8. What can you say about the effect of color in this activity?

Heat Lamp, Sheets of Paper, and Thermometers

For Problem Solvers: In the above activity you compared heat absorption from white paper and black paper. Find several different colors of paper. Use only paper that is the same except for color. Construction paper will work well. From what you have already learned, predict which colors will absorb the most heat from the light bulb and which will reflect the most heat. Arrange the papers in order, according to your predictions. Design an investigation to find out if your predictions are accurate.

Were you right? Why is it important that you don't use construction paper for some colors, typing paper for some colors, and art paper for still other colors?

That raises another interesting question—does one *type* of paper absorb more heat than another? Now, to test that question, what will you do about color?

Teacher Information

Dark materials have a greater tendency to absorb heat than do lighter-colored materials. The thermometers behind the two sheets of paper will verify this tendency.

On a sunny day, direct sunlight could be used instead of the heat lamp. As an enrichment (or perhaps introductory) activity, invite students to go to the parking lot (on a warm day) and feel the surfaces of cars of various colors. Which colors tend to be warmest? This needs to be carefully supervised to avoid offending car owners.

Your "problem solvers" will enjoy the challenge of some real science, while they test the variables of color and types of paper with respect to heat absorption.

INTEGRATING: Math

SKILLS: Observing, inferring, classifying, measuring, predicting, communicating, comparing and contrasting, using space-time relationships, formulating hypotheses, identifying and controlling variables, experimenting

Activity 16.2
WHAT HAPPENED TO THE PENCIL?

 Take home and do with family and friends.

Materials Needed

- Clear tumbler or bowl
- Water
- Pencil (or spoon)

Procedure

1. Fill the tumbler or bowl about two thirds full of water.
2. Put the pencil into the water.
3. Look at the pencil from the top and from the side.
4. What appears to happen to the pencil at the water level? What ideas do you have about this effect?

Teacher Information

Light travels at different speeds through different substances, creating a bending effect on any light rays that enter a substance at an angle. This is called *refraction*. Light travels faster through air than it does through water. The bending of the light rays as they pass from air to water or from water to air results in an optical illusion as the object in the water appears to be broken at the surface of the water.

SKILLS: Observing, inferring

Activity 16.3
WHAT AFFECTS THE QUALITY OF REFLECTION?

Materials Needed

- Tin can
- Damp cloth
- Dry cloth
- Toothpaste
- Sandpaper

Procedure

1. Polish the bottom of the can by rubbing it with toothpaste, using a damp cloth. Shine it with a dry cloth.
2. Look at your reflection in the polished surface.
3. Scuff the polished surface lightly with the sandpaper.
4. Look at your reflection again.
5. Explain the difference in your reflection before and after the sandpaper treatment. What made the difference? Why do you think this happened?

For Problem Solvers: Find a variety of surfaces to shine the light on and compare reflections. Try a mirror, clear glass, textured glass, as is often used in bathroom windows, and other surfaces. Try a painted wall. You can see the reflection if you will tap two dusty chalkboard erasers together in the path of the light.

Teacher Information

A polished surface reflects light rays in a consistent pattern. A rough surface diffuses light rays (reflects them in all directions), preventing a clear focus.

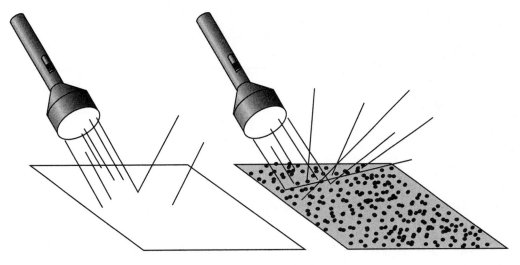

Two Flashlights, Two Surfaces

SKILLS: Observing, inferring, classifying, measuring, predicting, communicating, comparing and contrasting, identifying and controlling variables, experimenting

Activity 16.4
WHAT IS THE DIFFERENCE BETWEEN REFLECTED LIGHT AND SOURCE LIGHT?

Materials Needed

- Mirror

Procedure

1. Look briefly at the light in your room.
2. Now hold the mirror so that you can see the room lights in the mirror.
3. Which of these is the "source light" and which is "reflected light"?
4. If you were to cover the source light, what would happen to the reflected light?
5. If you cover the reflected light, what happens to the source light?
6. Light from your desk enables you to see the desk. Is it source light or reflected light?
7. Does the sun give off source light or reflected light? What about the moon? Explain.

Teacher Information

We receive light by two means—from sources that produce light and from objects that reflect light. There are relatively few sources of direct light (source light); everything else we see gives off reflected light. Light sources include light bulbs, fluorescent light tubes, burning matches and other fire, and the sun. Other objects can be seen only when there is light to be reflected from one or more of these sources.

SKILLS: Observing, inferring, comparing and contrasting

Activity 16.5
WHAT IS REFLECTED LIGHT?

Materials Needed

- Projector or flashlight
- Two chalkboard erasers
- Mirror
- Darkened room

Procedure

1. Arrange the projector and the mirror so that the light from the projector can be focused on the mirror.
2. With the room darkened, shine the projector light on the mirror at an angle.
3. Clap the chalkboard erasers together lightly in the beam of light and notice the angle of the light beam as it approaches and as it leaves the mirror. How do they compare?
4. Change the position of the projector so the light from the projector shines toward the mirror from different angles. Use chalk dust as needed to keep the light beam visible.
5. Each time you change the position of the projector, compare the angle of the light beam approaching the mirror to the angle of the reflected light beam.

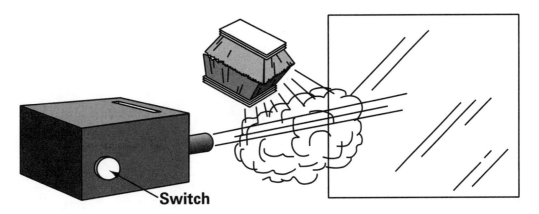

Projector, Mirror, and Two Chalkboard Erasers

Teacher Information

When light is reflected from a mirror, it is always reflected at the same angle as the angle of the light from the source to the mirror. In other words, the angle of reflection is always equal to the angle of incidence (approaching angle).

SKILLS: Observing, inferring, comparing and contrasting, formulating hypotheses, identifying and controlling variables, experimenting

Activity 16.6
HOW IS LIGHT REFLECTION LIKE THE BOUNCE OF A BALL?

Materials Needed

- Rubber ball
- Darkened room
- Mirror
- Flashlight or projector

Procedure

1. Bounce the ball from the floor as straight as you can.

2. Now bounce the ball to your partner.

3. Try bouncing the ball at different angles. Notice the angle of the ball's path as it approaches the floor and compare it with the angle of its path as it leaves the floor. How do they compare?

4. Now place the mirror on the floor and "bounce" the light from the flashlight off the mirror, first shining the light straight down at the mirror, then at different angles.

5. Compare the angles of light approaching and leaving the mirror. How do they compare with the angles of the bouncing ball approaching and leaving the floor?

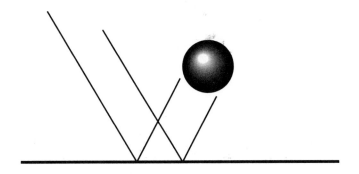

Figure 16.6-1

Bouncing Ball

287

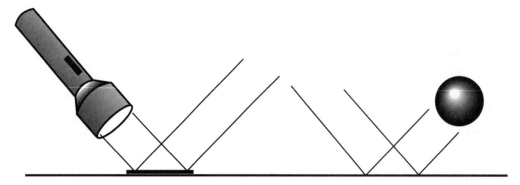

Figure 16.6-2

Bouncing Ball and Reflecting Light

For Problem Solvers: Does a "crazy ball" follow the same path when it bounces as light does when it is reflected? Try it.

Teacher Information

The purpose of the activity of bouncing the ball is to provide a familiar model. The student should notice that the angle of incidence (angle of the ball's path as it approaches the floor) equals the angle of reflection (angle of the ball's path as it leaves the floor). To avoid the curve in the ball's path, created by the force of gravity, put a table next to a wall and roll the ball across the table to the wall.

INTEGRATING: Math

SKILLS: Observing, inferring, measuring, predicting, comparing and contrasting, formulating hypotheses, identifying and controlling variables

Activity 16.7
HOW MANY IMAGES CAN YOU SEE?

(Teacher-supervised activity)

Materials Needed

- Two mirrors, one with a peephole in the center
- Small object

Procedure

1. Hold the two mirrors a few centimeters (inches) apart with the reflecting surfaces facing each other (Figure 16.7-1).

2. Hold a small object between the mirrors and look at it through the peephole (Figure 16.7-2).

3. What do you see?

4. Hold the object in different positions and tilt the mirrors at different angles.

5. Explain what you see and why you think it happens.

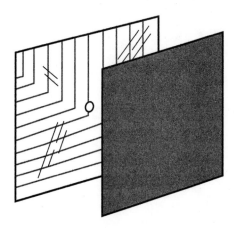

Figure 16.7-1

Two Mirrors Facing Each Other, with a Peephole in One

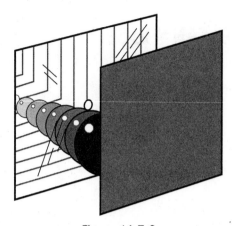

Figure 16.7-2

A Small Object Held Between the Mirrors

Teacher Information

To prepare the peephole mirror, use a knife to scrape away the silvering from the back of one mirror to form a small peephole about a centimeter (half inch) in diameter right in the center of the mirror.

As light is reflected from one mirror to the other, an infinite number of images can be seen if the mirrors are kept parallel to each other. As the mirrors are held at a slant with respect to each other, fewer images will be seen because the slant brings the image closer to the top of the mirror with each reflection.

SKILLS: Observing, inferring, comparing and contrasting

Activity 16.8
HOW WELL CAN YOU CONTROL THE REFLECTION OF LIGHT?

(Upper grades)

Materials Needed

- Projector or flashlight
- Several partners
- One mirror for each person
- Darkened room

Procedure

1. Arrange the people with mirrors in a pattern such that light can be reflected from one to the other.
2. From what you know about the reflected angles of light, see if the group can direct the light from the projector to one mirror and have it reflected from the first mirror to a second mirror. From the second to a third?
3. Determine who will reflect the light to whom in order to reflect the projector light all around the group.
4. Pick a spot (target) on the wall opposite the last person and light up the target with reflected light. Be sure the light from the projector reflects from all mirrors before lighting up the target.
5. With the light reflecting from all mirrors, compare the angle of reflection (the light leaving the mirror) with the angle of incidence (the light approaching the mirror) for each mirror. If necessary, have someone stand in the middle and clap two chalkboard erasers together lightly to make the beams more visible.
6. How does the angle of reflection compare with the angle of incidence?

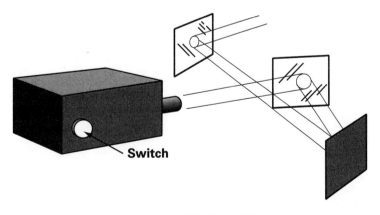

Projector and Series of Mirrors

For Problem Solvers: With three friends, each of you with a mirror, play a game of "Reflection Relay." Select a target and position yourselves to reflect the light from a projector through all four mirrors and hit the target. Time yourselves and see if you can improve your time with each new target you select. Challenge another group, and have a contest. Perhaps the entire class would like to get involved.

Teacher Information

Students will enjoy the challenge of reflecting the light from mirror to mirror in various patterns. They should notice that the angle of reflection and the angle of incidence are always equal.

Students who choose to try the reflected relay suggested in "For Problem Solvers" will acquire new insights with light and reflections. As they practice, they will learn that they need to stay near the light source and near one another, because the light spreads out and gets dimmer with distance. They will also learn to position themselves such that they are reflecting the light to one another as directly as possible, again to maximize brightness.

INTEGRATING: Math

SKILLS: Observing, measuring, predicting, communicating, comparing and contrasting, identifying and controlling variables, experimenting

Activity 16.9
HOW DOES A PERISCOPE WORK?

(Teacher-supervised activity for upper grades)

 Take home and do with family and friends.

Materials Needed

- Two 1-quart milk cartons
- Two mirrors (same width as milk carton)
- Knife or scissors
- Tape

Procedure

1. Cut the tops off both milk cartons.
2. Cut an opening about 5 cm (2 in.) in diameter in one side of each carton, near the bottom.
3. Tape a mirror in the bottom of each carton, facing the opening at a 45-degree angle.
4. Tape the cartons together at the open ends to make a long tube.
5. Look into the mirror at one end of your periscope. What do you see?
6. Can you put your periscope together in such a way that you can look behind you? To your right?

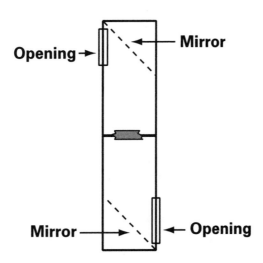

Milk Carton Periscope

For Problem Solvers: Design your own periscope. What can you do to make it longer? Can you make it so that you can turn it around 360 degrees, so you can see in any direction without turning yourself around? Do you need more mirrors in your design? Can you find round tubing, or something else that will work better than milk cartons?

Teacher Information

The periscope activity is likely to attract a lot of interest and could be used as an enrichment activity. It is an application of the concept of angle of reflection students learn about in other activities of this unit. Students might enjoy expanding their periscopes to include three, four, or more milk cartons to make the periscope longer or to give it creative shapes, as suggested in "For Problem Solvers." Additional mirrors might be needed as students expand with creative ideas. Other tubes could be substituted for the milk cartons. This is a good time to be creative.

INTEGRATING: Math

SKILLS: Observing, measuring, predicting, communicating, identifying and controlling variables, experimenting

Activity 16.10
HOW CAN YOU POUR LIGHT?

(Enrichment activity)

 Take home and do with family and friends.

Materials Needed

- Tall, slim olive jar with lid
- Flashlight
- Nail
- Masking tape or plastic tape
- Newspaper or light cardboard
- Hammer
- Water
- Sink or dishpan

Procedure

1. With the hammer and nail, make two holes in the lid of the jar. The holes should be near the edge but opposite each other. One hole should be quite small. Work the nail in the other hole to enlarge it a bit.

2. Fill the jar about two thirds full of water and put the lid on (Figure 16.10-1).

Figure 16.10-1

Jar with Lid On, Showing Two Different-sized Holes

3. Put tape over the holes in the lid until you are ready to pour.

4. Lay the jar and flashlight end to end, with the face of the flashlight at the bottom of the jar.

295

5. Roll the newspaper around the jar and flashlight to enclose them in a light-tight tube. Tape the tube together so it will stay (Figure 16.10-2).

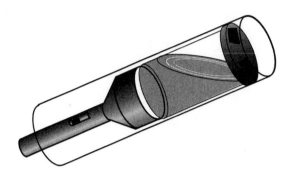

Figure 16.10-2

Flashlight and Jar Taped Together

6. Slide the flashlight out of the tube, turn it on, and slide it back into the tube. Darken the room.

7. Hold the apparatus upright and remove the tape from the lid. With the large nail hole down, pour the water into the sink (Figure 16.10-3).

8. What happened to the beam of light as the water poured into the sink?

9. Do you have any idea what caused this?

10. Share your ideas together.

Figure 16.10-3

Same System with Water Pouring from Larger Hole

For Problem Solvers: Use your creativity with this activity. Try different containers for the water, and different light sources. Try putting some food coloring in the water. Does that provide the same effect as if you put a colored filter (colored acetate) over the flashlight?

Teacher Information

Although light travels in straight lines, it is reflected internally at the water's inner surface and follows the path of the stream of water. Because of the phenomenon of internal reflection, fiber optics can be used to direct light anywhere a wire can go, even into the veins and arteries of the human body.

SKILLS: Observing, inferring, communicating

Activity 16.11
WHAT COLOR IS WHITE?

(Upper grades)

 Take home and do with family and friends.

Materials Needed

- White posterboard
- Compass
- String 1 m (1 yd.) long
- Crayons
- Scissors

Procedure

1. With your compass, draw a circle 15 cm (6 in.) in diameter on the posterboard.
2. Cut out the circle with the scissors.
3. Draw three equal pie-shaped sections on the posterboard and color them red, green, and blue.
4. Make two small holes near the center of the circle.

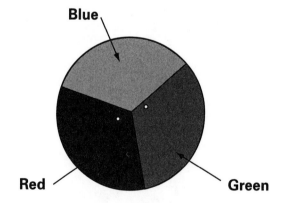

Divided and Colored Circle with Two Holes Punched

298

5. Thread the string through the holes (in one hole and out the other) and tie the ends of the string together, forming a loop that passes through the two holes of the disk.

6. Center the disk on the string loop and make the disk spin by alternately stretching and relaxing the string.

7. As the disk spins, watch the colored side.

8. What happens to the colors? Why do you think this happens?

For Problem Solvers: Try the same thing with more disks and different color combinations. Try using only two sections and coloring them with complementary colors, such as yellow and blue. Try several sections, alternating the same two colors back and forth and see if you get the same result as with two large sections. Each time you try a new design or color combination, make a prediction of what you will see as the disk spins—then try it, and test your prediction.

Teacher Information

As the primary colors spin, they should blend together to form a grayish white. If one of the colors seems to dominate, some of that color should be replaced with more of the other two colors. Blue might need a bit more than its share. Students will enjoy experimenting with various color combinations and testing their predictions of the resulting blends, as suggested in "For Problem Solvers."

The disk may spin better if its weight is increased by doubling the thickness of posterboard or pasting the disk onto cardboard or by gluing a button on the back of the disk. Another option is to mount the disk onto a sanding pad designed for a quarter-inch drill. The drill could then be used to spin the disk. If a drill is used, the disk must be secured well, as it could otherwise fly off and cause injury. This is less likely to happen if you use a drill with a variable-speed switch and avoid high speed.

INTEGRATING: Art

SKILLS: Observing, inferring, classifying, measuring, predicting, communicating, comparing and contrasting, identifying and controlling variables, experimenting

Activity 16.12
HOW CAN YOU SPIN DIFFERENT COLORS?

Materials Needed

- White posterboard
- Black fine-tipped marker
- Newspapers
- String l m (1 yd.) long
- Scissors
- Compass
- Pencil
- Ruler

Procedure

1. Use the compass to draw a circle on the posterboard 15 cm (6 in.) in diameter. Cut out the circle with the scissors (Figure 16.12-1).

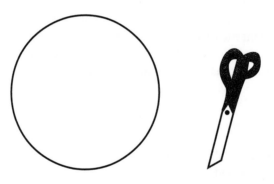

Figure 16.12-1

Circle Drawn on Paper, Scissors

2. Put a layer of several thicknesses of newspaper on the table and place your white disk on the newspaper.
3. With the fine-tipped marker, make one of the patterns shown in Figure 16.12-2. Let it dry.

Figure 16.12-2

Disk Patterns

4. Make two small holes on opposite sides of the center point, each about 1 cm (3/8 in.) from the center point (Figure 16.12-3).

Off center points   **Center point**

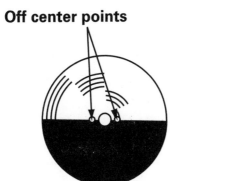

Figure 16.12-3

Center Point and Holes Marked on Patterns

5. Thread the string through the holes of the disk and tie the ends together.
6. Put one finger of each hand through the string, and wind up the disk on the string. Make the disk spin by successively pulling and relaxing the string.
7. As the disk spins, watch the painted side.
8. What do you see? Can you explain it?

For Problem Solvers: Create your own patterns for the disk. Yours might work out better than the ones shown here.

Teacher Information

When the retina receives repeated flashes of white light, they are interpreted by the brain as color. Such flashes of white light are produced by the spinning black-and-white disk. This phenomenon was discovered by Benham in the nineteenth century. If you have a phonograph turntable with adjustable speed, the effect can be studied by making a hole in the center of the disk and laying it on the turntable. Or attach the disk to a sanding pad for an electric drill, and turn the disk with the drill. Be sure the drill has a variable speed switch. **CAUTION: If it spins too fast, the disk could fly off and cause injury.**

INTEGRATING: Art

SKILLS: Observing, inferring, classifying, measuring, predicting, communicating, comparing and contrasting, identifying and controlling variables, experimenting

Topic 17: Sound

TO THE TEACHER

Sound is a very important part of our lives. It is one of the first stimuli to which newborn infants respond, and its presence or absence shapes and affects us throughout our entire lives. This section introduces sound, its causes and uses. A study of sound lends itself very well to concrete activities, with many possibilities for discovery/inquiry. No attempt is made to introduce the physiology of the ear, although you may choose to teach it in relation to this area.

A study of sound can be greatly expanded in the Language Arts to develop and enrich listening skills. Music can be integrated through discussion of musical terms found within this section. Activities on inventing and playing musical instruments could lead to additional study of ancient methods and modern electronic methods of producing music.

Throughout the study, children should be encouraged to bring and demonstrate their own musical instruments. If there is a high school or university nearby, the music director may be willing to cooperate in providing musicians and instruments. Most communities have choral groups that might be willing to perform. A note to parents asking for the names of family members or neighbors who play unusual musical instruments could produce interesting and entertaining results.

As the importance of sound is discussed, the value of being able to hear and speak clearly should be emphasized. Children should know that people of all ages suffer from hearing loss, and that almost everyone develops some degree of impairment as he or she grows older.

Sometime near the beginning of the study, the class should discuss, and perhaps list, ways sound can help us; for example, communication, warning, entertainment, aesthetics, and protection. Sound can also be harmful. Loud noise can injure the ears. Sound can be pleasing and soothing to an individual, but it can also be disturbing and irritating. The loudness of sound is measured in decibels. For public protection, many communities have laws restricting the decibel levels that can be produced by any means. With electronic sound equipment being so common, children should understand reasons for attempts to control noise levels.

In discussing pitch, or the frequency of vibrations, children should be aware that the human ear cannot detect the frequency of very high (fast) and very low (slow) vibrations. Dog whistles are too high pitched to be heard by people, but they can be heard by dogs and some other animals.

Resource people can be involved frequently in this study. These might include individuals of all ages who have hearing handicaps, a nurse, a doctor, an audiologist, an acoustics specialist, a music store owner, a musician, someone who makes or plays unusual musical instruments, or any others you may find helpful.

This is an area rich in "take home and do with family and friends" activities. Taking home concrete objects to show and talk about will help children develop increased language ability and be a source of strong motivation in science.

Activity 17.1
HOW CAN YOU MAKE MUSIC WITH FISH LINE?

 Take home and do with family and friends.

Materials Needed

- 50 cm (20 in.) of monofilament fish line with a wooden dowel 10 cm (4 in.) long attached to one end
- Additional dowel
- Shoe box with lid
- Toothpick
- Pencil

Procedure

1. Put the shoe box on the edge of a table or desk.
2. Remove the lid, make a hole in one end of the box with your pencil, thread the fish line through the hole, and secure it with the toothpick (Figure 17.1-1).

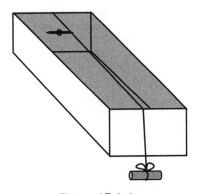

Figure 17.1-1
Open Shoe Box

3. Put the lid on the box and stretch the fish line lengthwise across the top of the box. Put the additional dowel under the fish line near one end of the lid (Figure 17.1-2).

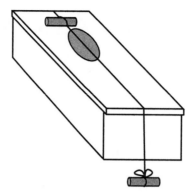

Figure 17.1-2

Box with Lid

4. Slowly pull down on the dowel and pluck the fish line. What do you hear? What do you see?

5. As you pluck the line, pull down on the dowel to stretch it tighter. Watch and listen. What do you see? What do you hear? Try to play a simple tune. What might happen if you cut a hole in the lid of the shoe box? Try it.

For Problem Solvers: Experiment with different materials for the string on your home-made instrument. Try different types and weights of fish line, string, fine wire, or whatever is available. Which one can you get the highest notes with? Which one can you get the low-est notes with?

Teacher Information

This activity should help children discover the relationship between the rate (speed) of vibration and the pitch (high-low) of sound. You may want to relate this activity to the previous one with rubber bands. The hole cut in the lid will increase the resonance. Resonance is a way of increasing the intensity of a sound by causing one object (vibrating fish line) to create a sympathetic vibration of about the same frequency in another object (the walls of the shoe box).

The dowel on the top of the lid serves as a bridge to keep the string elevated enough to vibrate freely; stringed instruments use the same principles. A guitar, violin, cello, or viola could be used for comparison.

INTEGRATING: Music

SKILLS: Observing, classifying, measuring, predicting, communicating, comparing and con-trasting, identifying and controlling variables, experimenting

Activity 17.2
HOW DO YOU MAKE SOUNDS WITH YOUR VOICE?

Materials Needed

- Prepared shoe box from Activity 17.1

Procedure

1. Hold your fingers on the front of your throat.

2. Hum and talk. Make high sounds and low sounds. Make soft sounds and loud sounds. What happened? Can you feel a difference?

3. Pluck the string stretched across the shoe box. Make it tighter as you continue to pluck. What happens?

4. Can you explain how your vocal cords work?

For Problem Solvers: Can you make a sound with your shoe-box guitar that is higher than your voice? Can you make a sound with your shoe-box guitar that sounds about the same pitch as your voice? Can you make the pitch of your voice higher? Can you make it lower?

What do you do with your shoe-box guitar to make the sound higher or lower? What do you think you do with your voice to make it higher or lower? Do something to find out—read from the encyclopedia or another book you can find. Ask someone who you think would know.

Teacher Information

Our vocal cords are caused to vibrate by air passing over them. Muscles in our throat tighten and loosen the cords to produce higher and lower sounds. The amount of air we pass by the cords determines loudness and softness. This is a reason proper breathing technique is so important to singers.

INTEGRATING: Music

SKILLS: Observing, inferring, classifying, measuring, predicting, communicating, comparing and contrasting, identifying and controlling variables, experimenting, researching

Activity 17.3
HOW CAN SOUNDS BE SHAPED?

 Take home and do with family and friends.

Materials Needed

- Paper and pencils

Procedure

1. Take a deep breath and hum a note. Hold the note while you slowly open your mouth as wide as you can.

2. Hold your tongue and say some words.

3. Let go of your tongue and say the phrase "black bug's blood" rapidly several times.

4. List ways we change or "shape" the sounds our vocal cords make.

5. How many ways can you imitate how your parents call you to come home, or to get ready for school?

For Problem Solvers: In this activity you changed the sound of your voice by changing your mouth and by holding your tongue. Try to change the sound of your voice with your hands. Hold your hands over your mouth and make a long sound with your voice. Change the shape of your hands and see how much you can change your voice.

Speak into a box, into a garden hose, into other things. How many ways can you think of to change the sound of your voice?

Teacher Information

Our vocal cords produce pitch and loudness of sound, but we depend on our throat, mouth, tongue, and teeth to produce the phonetic "shaping" of the sounds. This ability to produce phonetic differences is one of the reasons we are able to develop the highly complex, interrelated process we call vocal communication.

For enrichment, introduce a unit on nonverbal communication in social studies or language arts.

INTEGRATING: Language arts, social studies, music, physical education

SKILLS: Observing, predicting, communicating, comparing and contrasting, identifying and controlling variables, experimenting

Activity 17.4
HOW CAN YOU MAKE BOTTLED MUSIC?

 Take home and do with family and friends.

Materials Needed

- Eight glass soda bottles of the same size and shape
- Water
- Paper slips numbered 1 to 8
- Pencil

Procedure

1. Pour water to different levels in the bottles.
2. Blow gently across the tops of the bottles until a sound is produced for each one. Arrange the bottles in a row according to the pitch of the sound from low to high.
3. You may want to add to or remove water from the bottles to make a musical scale. Under each bottle put a slip of paper numbered from one to eight.
4. Try to play a simple tune by blowing across the tops of the bottles. Can you decide what is vibrating to make the sound?
5. Use a pencil to tap the side of each bottle near the top. What happened? Check the numbers from low to high. What is vibrating to make the sound? What can you say about this?

For Problem Solvers: Try to tune the bottles to the piano. Can you make one of the bottles produce the same pitch as one of the piano keys? Can you match the piano with one full octave of sounds from the bottles? One octave is eight white keys in a row. If you are using bottles with lids, put the lids on overnight and see if the sounds still match the next morning.

Teacher Information

To do this activity, children may need to be reminded of the musical meaning of the term *pitch*.

In steps 1–4, blowing across the bottle causes the air to vibrate. This is the way pipe organs and musical wind instruments produce sound. A longer column of air will cause a slower vibration and a lower pitch. When the bottles are struck in step 5, it is the glass that vibrates to produce the sound. Water will slow the rate of vibration of the glass. Therefore, the greater the amount of water, the more slowly the glass vibrates, and the lower the pitch.

Remember, water expands and contracts according to its temperature. Water also evaporates. Both of these factors may make the bottles change pitch if they are kept for later use.

INTEGRATING: Music

SKILLS: Observing, classifying, measuring, predicting, communicating, comparing and contrasting, identifying and controlling variables, experimenting

Activity 17.5
HOW CAN YOU MAKE MUSIC WITH TUBES?

 Take home and do with family and friends.

Materials Needed

- Drinking straws
- Garden hose 1 m long
- Scissors
- Mouthpiece from a bugle, trumpet, or trombone

Procedure

1. Cut one end of a drinking straw to a point. Moisten the cut end and put it between your lips. Blow gently around the straw. Cut pieces from the end of the straw as it is being played. What happened? What can you say about this?

Drinking Straw with End Cut to a Point

2. Place a mouthpiece in a garden hose. Blow into the mouthpiece to see if you can make a sound. Change the shape of the hose. What happens to the pitch of the sound?

3. Try it without the mouthpiece. Can you make the same sounds?

For Problem Solvers: Making musical sounds with the soda straw and with the garden hose probably gave you lots of new ideas for making still more musical sounds. Try your ideas. Get several different kinds and sizes of soda straws and do whatever you can do with them to make new sounds.

Put a skinny straw into a fat straw and slide them in and out as you play notes. What happened?

Cut one or more holes along the top of a straw and make more new sounds. Can you play it like a flute?

Teacher Information

With practice, the students will be able to make the cut end of the straw vibrate to produce sound. This is similar to a clarinet or oboe. Paper straws work better than plastic because the plastic does not compress as easily to form a reed. Plastic straws are very usable for this activity, however.

When the group uses the garden hose, a child who plays the trumpet, trombone, or bugle may be able to demonstrate and help others learn to play. Changing the shape of the hose will not vary the pitch; however, cutting a length off either the straw or the hose will shorten the vibrating column of air and raise the pitch.

INTEGRATING: Music

SKILLS: Observing, classifying, measuring, predicting, communicating, comparing and contrasting, identifying and controlling variables, experimenting

Activity 17.6
HOW CAN YOU MAKE A KAZOO WITH A COMB?

 Take home and do with family and friends.

Materials Needed

- Combs of various sizes
- Kazoos
- Tissue paper 10 cm × 20 cm (4 in. × 8 in.)

Procedure

1. Fold the tissue paper over the comb, letting it hang down each side.
2. Hum into the paper-wrapped comb. What happened? What can you say about this?
3. Hum a tune on the kazoo. How does it make a sound?
4. Raise your head so you are looking at the ceiling of the room. Hold your fingers on the front of your neck. Hum a tune. What happened? What can you say about this?

Teacher Information

Sounds are produced by vibrations. With the tissue paper and comb, sound is produced by the vocal cords, which in turn cause the paper over the comb to vibrate and alter the sound. The same occurs when a kazoo is used.

This activity can provide a review of the way sound is produced through vibration and how sounds can be altered through the vibration of another object.

Kazoos may be purchased in novelty stores that carry party noisemakers. Some music stores also carry them.

INTEGRATING: Music

SKILLS: Observing, measuring, communicating, identifying and controlling variables, experimenting

Activity 17.7
WHAT IS A TRIPLE-T KAZOO?

 Take home and do with family and friends.

Materials Needed

- Toilet-tissue tube
- Waxed paper (about twice the diameter of the tube)
- Rubber band
- Paper punch

Procedure

1. Punch a hole in one end of the toilet-tissue tube. Reach as far into the tube as you can with the paper punch.
2. Wrap the waxed paper over the other end (opposite the punched hole) and secure the waxed paper with the rubber band.
3. Hum into the open end of the tube.
4. Make music with others who are making kazoos and with other instruments of all kinds that have been made by the class.
5. Color your kazoo. Be creative, and make it just the way you want it to be.
6. Why do we call it the "Triple-T" kazoo? When you think you know, tell your teacher, but keep it a secret from those who are still trying to decide.

Teacher Information

The sounds, and change in pitch, are produced by the voice, but the kazoo gives it an interesting sound. Children will enjoy adding the Triple-T kazoo to their collection of homemade musical instruments.

Why do we call it the Triple-T kazoo? Because it's made from a **T**oilet **T**issue **T**ube, of course!

INTEGRATING: Music, art

SKILLS: Observing

Activity 17.8
HOW CAN YOU SEE YOUR VOICE?

Materials Needed

- Cardboard oatmeal drum or medium-sized tin can
- 2-cm × 2-cm (1-in. × 1-in.) mirror
- Glue
- Screen or white surface
- Flashlight
- Heavy rubber band (or string)

Procedure

1. Remove both ends from a can or cardboard container (be careful of sharp edges).
2. Stretch a balloon over one end of the can and secure it with the rubber band. You now have a simple drum.
3. Glue the mirror to the center of the drum head.
4. Darken the room and have a friend shine a flashlight on the mirror, so the light is reflected onto a screen or wall.
5. Speak in a loud voice into the can and observe the reflected light on the wall.
6. Make different sounds to see what happens.

For Problem Solvers: Hold the drum over the speaker of a stereo while you play music on the stereo and shine a flashlight onto the mirror. Turn the volume up and down. Watch the reflection on the wall. Do you see any difference when the volume changes? Do you see any difference with high notes and bass notes? Try a different musical selection. Try a different stereo if you have another one available. Is there any difference?

Can you think of any other ways to observe vibrations that are caused by sound waves?

Teacher Information

When the child shouts into the can, the drum head will vibrate, causing the reflected pattern on the wall to change shape. Different sounds will cause different shapes. This is a method of changing sound waves into light so they may be observed. It is a simple oscilloscope. This principle is used in many technical fields, such as medicine. Musical groups often use this principle to produce light shows to accompany their music. Your encyclopedia can provide additional information if children would care to explore this topic in greater depth.

INTEGRATING: Music

SKILLS: Observing, measuring, predicting, communicating, comparing and contrasting, identifying and controlling variables, experimenting

Activity 17.9
WHAT CAN WATER TELL US ABOUT SOUND?

Materials Needed

- Box of dominoes
- Pan of water
- Small rock
- Drawing paper
- Crayons

Procedure

1. Stand the dominoes on end on a solid surface approximately 3 cm (1 in.) apart.

2. Tip the first domino forward so it hits the one next to it. What happened?

3. Matter is made up of tiny particles called molecules that react very much as the dominoes did when the first one was disturbed. Energy in the form of vibration is transferred from one molecule to another.

4. Drop a small rock into a pan of water. Observe what happens to the water. When molecules bump against one another, they transfer energy to all the other molecules around them, causing vibrations to travel in all directions.

5. Can you draw a picture of the way you think sound travels in air? Try it, and show your picture to your teacher.

Teacher Information

The use of dominoes will help children see how energy is transferred from one object to another. The pan of water should show how the energy is transferred in all directions (in this case, in ripples). If a large pan is used, the children may observe that the ripples bounce off solid objects and reverse direction. Echoes are caused by sound waves traveling out and bouncing back in waves.

INTEGRATING: Music

SKILLS: Observing, measuring, predicting, communicating, identifying and controlling variables, experimenting

Activity 17.10
HOW CAN A THREAD HELP CARRY YOUR VOICE?

 Take home and do with family and friends.

Materials Needed

- Two paper cups
- Toothpick
- Cotton thread, about 4 m (4 yds.) long

Procedure

1. Use the toothpick or your pencil to punch a small hole in the center of the bottom of each cup.

2. Push one end of the thread through the hole of each cup.

3. Break the toothpick in half and tie each end of the thread to one piece of toothpick so the thread cannot pull out of the hole in the cup.

4. Keep the thread tight and be sure it doesn't touch anything.

5. Put the cup to your ear and have your friend talk into his or her cup. Now you talk and have your friend listen. Now whisper.

6. What happened? What happens when you touch the thread? Explain why you think this happens. Make a set of telephones at home and show them to your family.

For Problem Solvers: Make a "party line" by crossing the lines from two sets of telephones over each other. Three people can then listen while one person talks. See if you can include a third set of telephones.

Teacher Information

This is an inexpensive way to provide a telephone for each student in your class to take home and tell about. The telephone works in a very simple way. Sound waves cause the bottom of the first cup to vibrate. These vibrations, in turn, cause the thread to vibrate. The vibrating thread causes the bottom of the other cup and the air inside to vibrate. The sounds the students hear are a result of these vibrations; the air in the second cups strikes their eardrums in nearly the same way it struck the bottom of the first cups as their partners spoke into them.

Use heavy cotton thread. Polyester is easier to find, but it tangles easily. Dental floss is an excellent substitute, but more expensive.

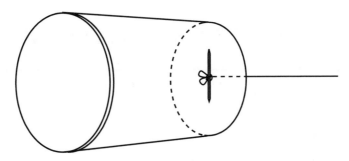

Paper Cup with Toothpick and Thread

INTEGRATING: Music

SKILLS: Observing, measuring, predicting, communicating, identifying and controlling variables, experimenting

Activity 17.11
HOW WELL DOES SOUND TRAVEL THROUGH WOOD?

 Take home and do with family and friends.

Materials Needed

- Table (or desk)

Procedure

1. Have a partner tap an object on the table or desk loudly enough for you to hear.
2. Put your ear on the desk top and have your partner tap again.
3. What happened?
4. What can you say about this?
5. If anyone in the class has a ticking wristwatch, see if you can hear it through the table.
6. What can you say about sound traveling through solid objects? Can you think of a reason for this?
7. What does the statement "Keep your ear to the ground" mean? Where do you think it began?

Teacher Information

Sound travels better through solid objects because the molecules are more tightly packed and don't have to move a great distance to bump against one another and transmit the vibrations. Sound will travel a greater distance in solids for the same reason. The exception, of course, is specially designed acoustic materials that appear to be solid but are designed with many spaces to "trap" vibrations.

The tapping on the desk will be heard more clearly when the ear is against the desk.

Native Americans used this principle, literally keeping their ears to the ground, to hear sounds at great distances. Buffalo herds and horses' hooves could be heard before they were seen. "Keep your ear to the ground" has come to mean "listen carefully."

INTEGRATING: Social studies

SKILLS: Observing, predicting, communicating, identifying and controlling variables

Activity 17.12
HOW CAN YOU MAKE A COAT HANGER SING?

 Take home and do with family and friends.

Materials Needed

- Metal coat hanger
- Two heavy cotton strings 50 cm (20 in.) in length

Procedure

1. Tie the strings to the wide ends of the hanger.

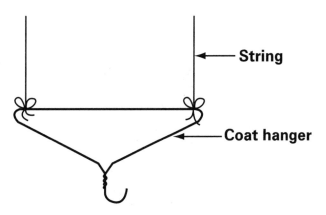

Coat Hanger with Two Strings

2. Hold the ends of the strings and hit the hanger against a solid object, such as your desk. Listen to the sound it makes.
3. Wrap the ends of the string around each of your index fingers. Put your fingers in your ears and tap the hanger on the solid object again.
5. Compare the first sound with the one you just heard.
4. What caused the sound? Discuss your ideas with your group.

For Problem Solvers: Were you surprised about the sound you heard from the coat hanger? Investigate this idea further. What variables could you change? Can you substitute something else for the coat hanger, such as a spoon, a piece of wire, another kind of coat hanger, or something else? Could you use a lighter or heavier string, or one of a different length, or a thin wire, or something else? Try tapping it against various objects and surfaces as well.

How does a doctor's stethoscope work? Do some research and find out. Do you see any relationship between the coat hanger activity and the stethoscope? Explain. Did you know that mechanics also use stethoscopes? The mechanic's stethoscope usually has a narrow probe sensor instead of a broad pad. Think of ways that you think a stethoscope might be helpful to a mechanic. Now back to the research—find out if you were right.

Teacher Information

When struck without the fingers in the ears, the hanger will sound flat and metallic. When the fingers are placed in the ears, the sound will be a loud gong because sound travels better through the relatively solid string than through the air.

INTEGRATING: Music

SKILLS: Observing, measuring, predicting, communicating, comparing and contrasting, identifying and controlling variables, experimenting

Activity 17.13
FROM HOW FAR AWAY CAN YOU HEAR A CLOCK TICK?

 Take home and do with family and friends.

Materials Needed

- Ticking clock
- Foot ruler
- Meter stick
- String
- Paper-cup telephone from Activity 17.10

Procedure

1. Listen to the clock tick. Move it as far from your ear as you can and still hear the ticking. Have a partner measure the distance.

2. Put one end of the foot ruler to your ear and the clock at the other end, touching the ruler. What happened?

3. Repeat step 2 using a meter stick. Substitute string for the meter stick. What happened?

4. Put the clock against one end of your paper-cup telephone and listen on the other end. What can you say about this? Can you see a relationship between this activity and the one with the hanger?

5. The sticks should not be held firmly or clutched in your hand. Why?

For Problem Solvers: Find a long board—preferably a 1″ × 2″ that is 8 feet long. Be sure you have your measurement recorded from #1 above, which indicates how far away you could hear the clock tick through the air. Put the board against your ear and have a friend put the clock against the board. Move the clock farther away until you can no longer hear it. Measure this distance and write it down. Could you hear the clock from any farther away through the board than you could through the air? Does sound travel better through air or through solids?

Teacher Information

Thin pieces of wood such as lathing of different lengths may be substituted for the foot ruler and meter sticks. The objects should not be held firmly, as the hand will absorb the vibrations and muffle the sound. The same phenomenon occurs when the thread on the paper-cup telephone is touched.

For your problem solvers, 1″ × 2″ lumber is called furring, and it is easy to find at all lumber stores or home improvement stores. Any long, thin board will do just fine.

INTEGRATING: Math

SKILLS: Observing, measuring, predicting, communicating, comparing and contrasting, identifying and controlling variables, experimenting

Activity 17.14
HOW FAST DOES SOUND TRAVEL?

Materials Needed

- Drum, cymbals, large metal lid or something else that will make a loud sound when visibly struck
- Stick to strike object

Procedure

1. Take your drum or other object out on the school grounds. Ask other members of the class to go with you.

2. Move about 100 meters (or about 100 yards) or more away from the other students.

3. Strike the object several times so the others can see the movement of your arm and hear the sound.

4. Remember, when you see an object move at a distance, you are seeing reflected light travel. When you hear the sound, you are hearing sound vibrations.

5. Tell what you observed. What can you say about the speed of light and the speed of sound?

For Problem Solvers: Using a stopwatch, have someone strike a metal post with a hammer from 100 meters away. Figure out a way to measure the distance. A greater distance (200 or 300 m) would be even better, but be sure you know how far it is. Start the stopwatch when you see the hammer strike the pole, and stop it when you hear the hammer strike the pole. Check the time several times for accuracy. Figure out how far sound travels in one second. How long does it take sound to travel one kilometer? Translate that to miles—how long does it take sound to travel one mile?

Teacher Information

Light travels very rapidly—over 186,000 miles a second. By comparison, sound is a slowpoke, moving at about 760 miles per hour at sea level. (Speed of sound is affected by temperature and density of the air. The speed range at sea level is about 740 to 780 as the temperature ranges from freezing to 75 degrees Fahrenheit.) Even at the short distance of 100 meters, it will be possible to see the child strike the drum before the sound is heard. Children who have been to athletic events in a large stadium may have noticed that movements that produce sounds on the playing field by athletes or bands are seen before the sounds are heard. Airplanes, especially fast jets, are sometimes difficult to locate in the sky by their sound because the sound is traveling so much more slowly that by the time it arrives, the plane has moved to a new position. Discuss these questions: (a) Would humidity affect the speed of sound? (b) Would sound travel faster through air or through water? (c) Would sound travel better on a cold day or on a hot day?

The speed of sound is not affected by loudness or frequency. Sound travels at about 330 meters per second in dry air at freezing point. Water vapor in the air increases the speed of sound slightly. However, sound travels faster in warm air than in cold air because air molecules are moving faster and therefore bump into one another more frequently. At room temperature, sound travels at about 340 meters per second, increasing about 0.6 meters per second for every degree rise in temperature above zero degrees Celsius. In water sound travels about four times as fast as it does in air, and in steel it travels about 15 times as fast as in air.

SKILLS: Observing, inferring, measuring, predicting, communicating, using space-time relationships, formulating hypotheses, identifying and controlling variables, experimenting

Activity 17.15
HOW CAN SOUND BE CONTROLLED?

Materials Needed

- Two identical shoe boxes
- Scissors
- Other materials or fabrics
- Foam rubber (1 inch thick)
- Glue (optional)
- Small paper cups (optional)

Procedure

1. Punch or cut a round hole approximately 2 cm (1 in.) in both ends of each shoe box. Try to make the holes nearly the same in both boxes.

2. Cut foam rubber to line the sides, top, and bottom of one shoe box. (Be sure to cut holes in the foam rubber to match the ones in the box.)

3. Measure and cut three pieces of foam rubber so they will fit from the bottom to the top of the shoe box and about halfway across, as shown in the following illustration.

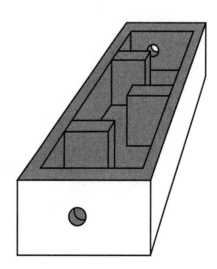

Foam-lined Shoe Box with Foam Dividers

324

4. Put the lid on each shoe box and have a friend whisper something to you through each box. Then have your friend speak more loudly and make other kinds of sounds. Be sure your friend's mouth and your ear are against the box when the sounds are made. You may want to glue a small paper cup, with the bottom removed, over the holes in the ends. This will help collect the sound.

5. What happened? What can you say about this?

6. Try lining other shoe boxes with different materials.

Teacher Information

This activity will help children discover one way of deadening sound. Sound waves, traveling through the air, strike the many holes in the foam rubber. The sound is reflected in many directions by the distorted surface, and the result is a muffling of the sound. Sound traveling through the foam-lined box will be mostly absorbed, while it will transfer clearly through the empty box, or even be amplified by it.

INTEGRATING: Music

SKILLS: Observing, inferring, measuring, predicting, communicating, comparing and contrasting, identifying and controlling variables, experimenting

Activity 17.16
WHAT HAPPENS TO SOUND WHEN THERE ARE FEWER MOLECULES?

(Teacher-supervised activity)

Materials Needed

- 4- to 8-ounce glass jar with tight-sealing lid
- Thread or string
- Hot (not boiling) water
- Small bell
- Tape

Procedure

1. Use the string to suspend the bell in the jar by taping it to the inside of the lid. Be sure the bell does not touch the sides or bottom of the jar.
2. Gently shake the jar and listen to the bell.
3. Remove the lid with the bell attached and carefully pour about 2–3 cm (1 in.) of hot water into the jar.
4. Allow the jar to stand for about 30 seconds and then replace the lid. Be sure the bell does not touch the water.
5. Let the jar cool, then gently shake the jar again and listen to the bell.
6. What happened? What can you say about this?

Bell in Jar

For Problem Solvers: Find a junior high school science teacher or a high school physics teacher. Ask the teacher if he or she has a vacuum pump, and, if so, if he or she would show you the demonstration with the bell in a bell jar. The teacher will know what you mean. It will be similar to what you did for this activity, except that it uses an electric bell, and it's more effective because the vacuum pump removes more of the air. Perhaps you know a high school physics student who could arrange to borrow the equipment and demonstrate it for your class.

Teacher Information

Before hot water is poured into the jar, the children should be able to hear the bell clearly. Hot water in the jar will displace most of the air molecules with steam. With fewer air molecules in the bottle, sound vibrations will not travel as easily, so the bell will not sound as loud.

Discuss the problem of communication on the moon or any other place without air.

SKILLS: Observing, inferring, measuring, predicting, communicating, comparing and contrasting, identifying and controlling variables, experimenting

Activity 17.17
WHAT IS A TUNING FORK?

Materials Needed

- Tuning fork
- Small dish of water
- Soft rubber mallet or rubber heel from a shoe

Procedure

1. Hold the handle of the tuning fork in one hand and strike it with a rubber mallet or heel of a shoe. (CAUTION: You shouldn't hit the tuning fork with a hard object.)
2. Bring the double end near your ear. What happened?
3. Strike the tuning fork again. Touch the double end. What happened?
4. This time, after striking the tuning fork, lower it slowly into the dish of water. What happened?
5. Strike the tuning fork again. Gently touch the handle to a hard surface such as a table or desk.

For Problem Solvers: You noticed what happened when you touched the base of the tuning fork to the table. Experiment with the tuning fork to see if you can find other ways to make it louder. Try touching it to a box, the body of a guitar or violin, and other things. What materials and what shapes seem to have the greatest effect?

Teacher Information

Tuning forks may be obtained from music stores and science-supply houses. Children who play stringed musical instruments may have tuning forks for use in tuning their instruments. Specially designed tuning forks are often used by doctors for general hearing-screening tests. Each tuning fork is tuned to a certain pitch. The pitch depends on the thickness and length, and the material of which it is made.

Most tuning forks vibrate so rapidly that it is difficult to detect movement by looking at them. Your students will learn that when the tines of a vibrating fork are lowered slowly into a dish of water, the water will splash, demonstrating that vibration is occurring. When the handle of a vibrating fork is placed on a table or desk, the sound will be amplified. If the tuning fork is touched to a large paper cup, a shoe box, or the body of a stringed instrument, the sound will be amplified.

INTEGRATING: Music

SKILLS: Observing, inferring, predicting, communicating, comparing and contrasting, identifying and controlling variables, experimenting

Activity 17.18
HOW CAN YOU MAKE A GOBLET SING?

(Teacher demonstration)

Materials Needed

- Four to six good-quality glass goblets
- Water
- Vinegar

Procedure

1. Check the goblets carefully to be certain they have no cracked or chipped edges.

2. Add different amounts of water to each goblet (no more than half full). Put a few drops of vinegar in the water.

3. Firmly hold the goblet by the base with one hand. Moisten the fingers of your other hand with the vinegar water and rotate your fingers lightly around the rim of the goblet. What happened? Can you think why?

4. Try the other goblets. Can you describe what is happening?

For Problem Solvers: Take two goblets that are just alike. Be sure they are clean, dry, and that they have no chips or cracks around the rim. Place them about 30 cm (12 in.) apart. Hold one goblet steady while you moisten your finger with vinegar water and make this goblet sing. While it is producing a loud tone, grasp it firmly to stop the tone and immediately listen carefully to the other goblet. What do you hear? If you hear nothing from the other goblet, try it again.

Lift the lid of a piano and make a steady singing tone into the piano with your voice, while someone holds the sustain pedal down. Stop the tone and listen. What do you hear?

Place two guitars face to face, just a short distance apart. Be sure they have been tuned alike. Pluck one string of one guitar, then stop the vibration of that string by placing your hand over it and listen to the other guitar. What do you hear?

See what you can learn about *sympathetic vibrations*. Use your encyclopedias or other reference books.

Teacher Information

Great care should be exercised in performing this activity. The goblets must be of high quality and completely free of rough edges. When this activity is properly performed, the moist fingers will cause the glass to vibrate and produce a beautiful, clear tone. The combination of water and vinegar seems to produce just enough lubricant and friction to make the demonstration easier.

Your problem solvers will experiment with sympathetic vibrations. This means that the vibrations of one goblet will travel through the air and cause another glass to vibrate and produce the same tone. In order for this to occur, the condition of each glass must be almost exactly the same. Both should be dry, empty, and at the same temperature. Their physical appearance should be the same.

Sympathetic vibration may also be experienced by singing into a piano while holding the sustain pedal down. The vibrations of the voice will cause strings, tuned to the same pitch in the piano, to vibrate.

INTEGRATING: Music

SKILLS: Observing, inferring, classifying, predicting, communicating, formulating hypotheses, identifying and controlling variables, experimenting, researching

Activity 17.19
HOW CAN SOUNDS BE HEARD MORE CLEARLY?

 Take home and do with family and friends.

Materials Needed

- 4-ounce, 8-ounce, and 12-ounce paper (or plastic) cups
- Larger round tapered containers (such as popcorn drums)

Procedure

1. Remove the bottoms from the paper cups and other containers.

2. Choose two friends, select different-sized containers, and go outside.

3. Have your friends walk away from you in opposite directions for about 50 paces.

4. Take a small cup, point it between your friends and say "Hello" in a loud voice into the narrower end of the cup. Next, turn to face each friend and repeat the hello at about the same volume.

5. Now fit the three different-sized cups together as shown in the illustration and repeat step 4.

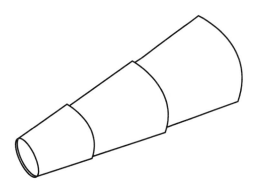

Paper Cups Nested to Form a Megaphone

6. Trade places with your friends and repeat the activities. Discuss your findings. Can you explain what happened?

For Problem Solvers: Do some investigating to see how many applications you can find for the megaphone. Who uses it? When? Why? Notice the shape of the end of a trumpet, where the sound leaves the trumpet. Is it shaped like a megaphone? Why? What other musical instruments use that shape?

Teacher Information

This activity is related to the activity with the paper-cup telephone. The object the children have produced is a megaphone, which collects, concentrates, and directs sound waves. The children on the playground will discover that they can hear better when the paper-cup megaphone is pointed toward them. They should also observe that as the megaphone is lengthened and widened, the sound is clearer. We often cup our hands around our mouths when we shout, for the same reason. Many wind instruments have bell-shaped ends.

INTEGRATING: Music

SKILLS: Observing, inferring, classifying, measuring, predicting, communicating, comparing and contrasting, formulating hypotheses, identifying and controlling variables, experimenting, researching

Activity 17.20
HOW CAN YOU PLAY A RECORD WITH A SEWING NEEDLE?

(Teacher-assisted activity)

Materials Needed

- 8-ounce paper cup
- Thin sewing needles
- Thimble
- Masking tape
- Sheet of 12-in. × 18-in. construction paper
- Old phonograph records
- Record turntable

Procedure

1. Have you done the paper-cup telephone activity yet? If not, perhaps you will want to try it before you begin this exploration. Ask your teacher about Activity 17.10.

2. Thomas Edison, a famous inventor, invented a talking machine that he called a phonograph. At first, a wax cylinder was used. It was later improved by making a round, hard disk. You can make a simple phonograph to play sound.

3. Very carefully, push a sewing needle through the lower lip of a paper cup so that the needle touches the bottom of the cup (Figure 17.20-1).

Figure 17.20-1

Paper Cup with Needle

4. Put an old phonograph record (it might get damaged) on a revolving turntable and hold the cup by two fingers while lightly touching the point of the needle to the grooves in the record (Figure 17.20-2). What happened?

Figure 17.20-2

Paper Cup on Phonograph Record

5. Form a sheet of construction paper into a cone held together with masking tape. Insert a sewing needle through the narrow part of the cone (Figure 17.20-3).

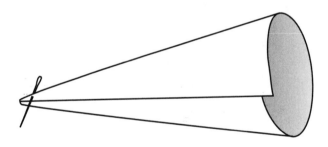

Figure 17.20-3

Needle Inserted Through Cone

6. Lightly touch the needle to the grooves of the record spinning on the turntable. What happened? Can you explain why?

For Problem Solvers: Identify variables that you think might affect the production of sound in this activity and experiment with those variables. Try various needles or other objects that you think might substitute for the needle. You could try many different ideas in the place of this particular paper cup. Can you think of another way to turn the record, so you don't need the turntable? Explore, and have fun learning about sound.

Think about what sound is. If there is sound, something is vibrating. Examine the record carefully with a hand lens. Use a microscope also if you have one. Can you tell what causes the needle to vibrate? Can you see anything that would cause it to change its vibrating pattern to create different sounds? Does a needle work any better for this than a straight pin? Examine the points and examine the grooves again. Look at the points of each under the microscope or hand lens while they are resting in a groove of the record. Which would you expect to work best? Why?

Teacher Information

This activity should be done individually or in small groups. The paper-cup telephone in Activity 17.10 demonstrates sound traveling better through solids and amplifying sound through concentrating the vibrations in a confined area (the paper cup). This activity is similar to the paper-cup telephone in many ways. The grooves in the record cause the needle to vibrate, which transfers to the bottom of the paper cup. The shape of the cup concentrates and amplifies the sound, making it possible to hear the sound reproduced from the grooves of the record. The paper cone works in the same way, except the sound may be louder due to the size of the cone and the better vibration that is possible through thinner material.

CAUTION: Young children will need help in inserting the needles and rolling the cones.

INTEGRATING: Music

SKILLS: Observing, inferring, communicating, comparing and contrasting, formulating hypotheses, identifying and controlling variables, experimenting

Activity 17.21

CAN YOU THINK OF WORDS THAT SOUND LIKE THE OBJECT OR ACTION THEY DESCRIBE?

(Enrichment activity)

Materials Needed

- Paper and pencils

Procedure

1. Some words in our language seem to sound like the object or event they describe. Say "bark" loudly and sharply. It seems to make a sound similar to the sound a dog makes. Now try the word "wolf." Say it sharply in a deep voice. What do you hear? Words that imitate the natural sound of the object or action involved are called onomatopoeia.

2. Get together with several friends and, beginning with the list below, see how many words you can find that make a noise similar to the object or event:

bark	creak
wolf	knock
bear	peep
croak	puff

3. Take your list home and ask members of your family to help add to it.

4. Compare your list with those of other members of the class.

5. Write an exciting story using as many onomatopoeia words as you can.

Teacher Information

Fairy tales, children's stories, and poetry make liberal use of onomatopoeia. The huffing and puffing of the wolf in "Three Little Pigs" is an excellent example. If children are conscious of the words and how words make them feel, their writing skills can be improved through this technique.

INTEGRATING: Language arts

SKILLS: Classifying, communicating

336

Activity 17.22
CAN YOU INVENT OR MAKE A MUSICAL INSTRUMENT?

(Teacher-assisted activity)

Materials Needed

- A variety of tubes, cans, rubber bands, and so on, that will produce sounds (see Figures 17.22-1, 17.22-2, and 17.22-3)

Procedure

1. Throughout history people have made and played musical instruments. The only rule seems to have been that the sound an instrument made was pleasing to the person playing it. Hollow logs were probably the first drums; reeds, the first wind instruments; and tough stems or dried animal parts such as tendons or intestines, the first stringed instruments. Today, some of our music is produced by electronics or other synthetic means. But many of the old ways of producing music are still being used, and some old ways of producing music are being revived. Most of the instruments being used in symphony orchestras of today were invented hundreds and even thousands of years ago.

2. You can invent and play your own musical instrument. Look at the illustrations here. These ideas should help you begin. Your instrument does not have to be the same. Maybe you can invent a better one.

3. When you have finished making your musical instrument, find some others who have made instruments and see if you can learn to play a tune together.

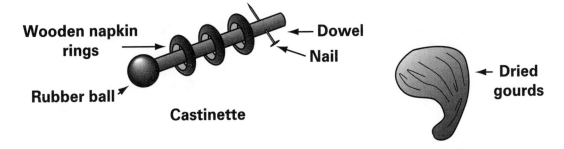

Figure 17.22-1

Homemade Percussion Instruments

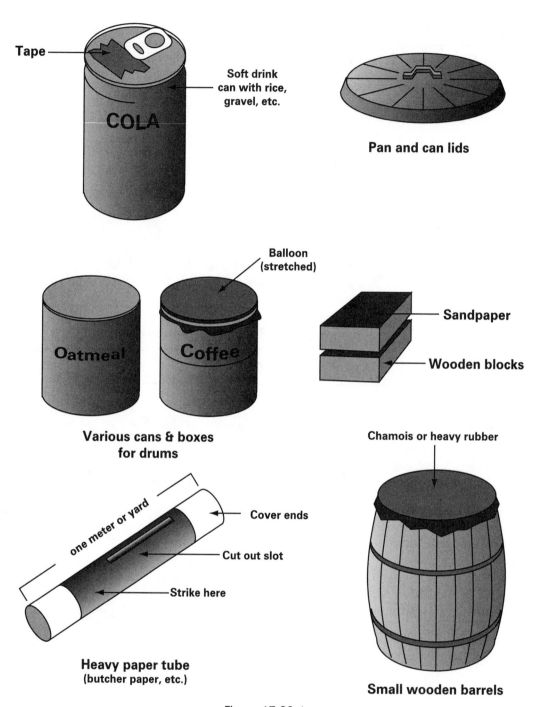

Tape

Soft drink
can with rice,
gravel, etc.

COLA

Pan and can lids

Balloon
(stretched)

Oatmeal

Coffee

Sandpaper

Wooden blocks

Various cans & boxes
for drums

Chamois or heavy rubber

one meter or yard

Cover ends

Cut out slot

Strike here

Heavy paper tube
(butcher paper, etc.)

Small wooden barrels

Figure 17.22-1

Homemade Percussion Instruments (continued)

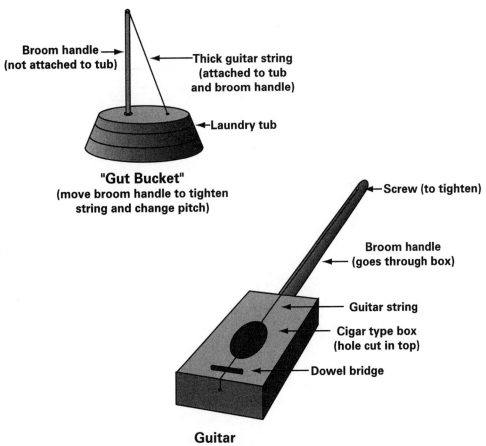

Broom handle ──→
(not attached to tub)

←── **Thick guitar string**
(attached to tub
and broom handle)

←──**Laundry tub**

"Gut Bucket"
(move broom handle to tighten
string and change pitch)

←── **Screw (to tighten)**

Broom handle
←── (goes through box)

──── **Guitar string**

──── **Cigar type box**
(hole cut in top)

──── **Dowel bridge**

Guitar
(tie loops of tough twine
around broom handle for frets)

Figure 17.22-2

Homemade Stringed Instruments

339

Hollow wood whistle

Straw ⟶

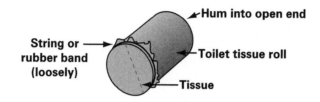

Hum into open end

String or
rubber band
(loosely) ⟶

Toilet tissue roll

Tissue

Figure 17.22-3

Homemade Stringed Instruments

Teacher Information

This activity can be used in conjunction with an art class or a music class. Encourage students to be creative as they make their instruments.

INTEGRATING: Music, art

SKILLS: Observing, inferring, classifying, measuring, predicting, communicating, comparing and contrasting, using space-time relationships, formulating hypotheses, identifying and controlling variables, experimenting, researching

Topic 18:   Simple Machines

TO THE TEACHER

Acquiring an understanding of simple machines can help open our eyes to the world around us. All machines, regardless of complexity, are composed of various combinations of the six simple machines. These are often applied in unique and creative ways, but they are nonetheless the same six. After some exposure to these activities, students will enjoy applying their newly acquired awareness in identifying the simple machines in common appliances and equipment—the shovel, the egg beater, the bicycle, the automobile, and so forth.

This section lends itself especially well to the discovery of scientific principles. Most of the activities suggested are safe for students to perform independently.

For most of the lever activities, a 1-in. board, which is approximately 1 m (1 yd.) long and 10 cm (4 in.) wide, is adequate. Others call for a lighter material, such as 1/2-in. plywood.

It is recommended that you prepare your levers by marking positions 1, 2, 3, 4, and 5, measured at equal intervals as indicated in Figure A.

Figure A

Lever with Points Marked and Eye Hooks

Eye hooks mounted at each point provide for attaching the spring balance.

Fulcrums ranging in height from 5 cm (2 in.) to 10 cm (4 in.) should be adequate and can be made by cutting a wedge shape from 4-in. × 4-in. post material (Figure B). Scraps that are adequate can usually be acquired at a lumber store for little or no cost.

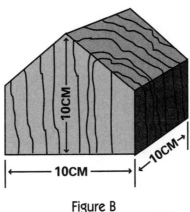

Figure B

4 in. × 4 in. Fulcrum

Activity 18.1
HOW DO STARTING FRICTION AND SLIDING FRICTION COMPARE?

 Take home and do with family and friends.

Materials Needed

- Two or three large books
- String 2 m (2 yds.) long
- Spring balance

Procedure

1. Tie the books into a bundle, using the string.
2. Place the books on a table or on the floor. Attach one end of the spring balance to the string wrapped around the books.

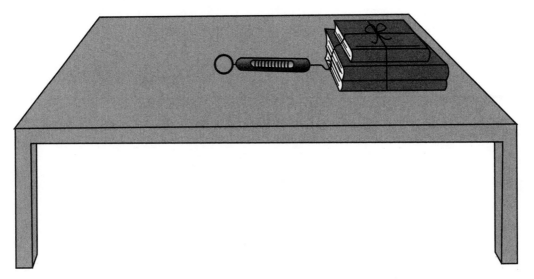

Bundled Books with Spring Balance Attached

3. Holding the other end of the spring balance and watching the indicator needle carefully, pull the books 50 to 100 cm (1.5 to 3 ft.) across the table (or floor).
4. What was the reading on the spring balance when the books first began to move?
5. What was the reading on the spring balance as the books moved steadily across the table?

6. Repeat the activity, being sure to pull the books in a steady, not jerking, manner.

7. Is the amount of force required to start the books moving equal to the amount of force needed to keep them moving? If not, which is greater?

8. Repeat to verify your findings.

9. Discuss your findings with others.

For Problem Solvers: Do you think friction will be the same for a stack of books if a small book is at the bottom of the pile as it will be if a large book is at the bottom? If you don't think it will be the same, which do you think will have the least friction? Do some scientific investigation and find out. Think through your procedure and discuss it with your teacher or someone else before you begin. Test the question for both starting friction and sliding friction.

Continue your investigation to compare the friction of various surfaces rubbing against each other. What could you put under the stack of books that you think would allow the books to slide across the table with less friction? Try at least two or three different materials and remember to test both starting friction and sliding friction. Make a graph of your results.

Teacher Information

Starting friction is greater than *sliding friction*. More force is required to start an object than to keep it sliding. One factor is inertia—the tendency of an object at rest to remain at rest and of an object in motion to remain in motion.

Those who accept the "For Problem Solvers" challenge will practice their skills at designing a simple experiment, interpreting the data, and communicating their results in the form of a graph. They will also learn some useful information about friction and the difference that is made by the type of surfaces involved.

INTEGRATING: Math

SKILLS: Observing, inferring, measuring, predicting, communicating, comparing and contrasting, formulating hypotheses, identifying and controlling variables, experimenting

Activity 18.2
HOW DOES ROLLING FRICTION COMPARE WITH SLIDING FRICTION?

 Take home and do with family and friends.

Materials Needed

- Two or three large books
- String 2 m (2 yds.) long
- Spring balance
- At least six round pencils

Procedure

1. Tie the books into a bundle, using the string.

2. Place the bundle of books on a table or on the floor.

3. Attach one end of the spring balance to the string wrapped around the books.

4. While holding the other end of the spring balance and watching the indicator needle carefully, slide the books steadily 25 to 50 cm (10 to 20 in.) across the floor (or table).

5. Record the amount of force needed for both starting friction and sliding friction.

6. Next place the pencils side by side, about 5 to 8 cm (2 to 3 in.) apart.

7. Place the books on the pencils at one end of the row.

8. Pull the books again with the spring balance and record the amount of force required for starting friction and rolling friction.

9. Did the pencils change the force needed to drag the books across the table? If so, how much difference did they make?

For Problem Solvers: Add this data to the graph that you prepared from your investigations in Activity 18.1.

Predict whether the starting friction and rolling friction will be the same with the books on a skateboard as with the pencils. Place the same books on a skateboard and compare both starting friction and rolling friction with the results you got when using the pencils. Add your skateboard data to your graph.

Teacher Information

Rolling friction is less than sliding friction. This principle is used in wheels and bearings in a wide variety of applications, from wheels under a table to the workings of complex machinery. The Egyptians probably used wheels as rollers to move large stones when they built the pyramids.

INTEGRATING: Math

SKILLS: Observing, inferring, measuring, predicting, communicating, comparing and contrasting, formulating hypotheses, identifying and controlling variables, experimenting

Activity 18.3
WHAT IS AN INCLINED PLANE?

Materials Needed

- Board at least 1.5 m (4.5 ft.) long
- Roller skate (or toy truck or small wagon)
- Cord or heavy string
- Pencil
- Spring balance
- Box of rocks (or books or other weights)

Procedure

1. Using the string, attach the load to the roller skate.
2. Weigh the load, including the roller skate, and record its weight.
3. Place the board on a stairway, with one end at the bottom of the stairs and the other end resting on the fourth step.
4. Attach the spring balance to the skate and pull the load up the inclined plane (board). As you pull steadily, notice the force indicated by the needle and record the results.

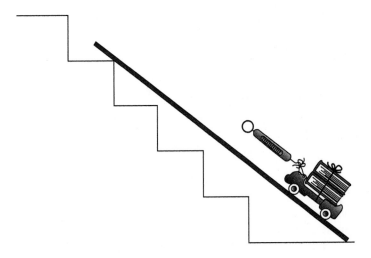

Figure 18.3-1

Roller Skate with Load on Inclined Plane

6. Compare the weight of the load with the force needed to pull the load up the inclined plane.

7. As you pulled the load up the inclined plane, was *more* force or *less* force required than the actual weight of the load? Record your answer.

8. Move the top of the board down to the first step (Figure 18.3-2).

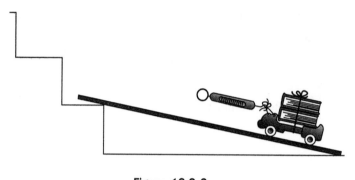

Figure 18.3-2

System in New Position

9. Judging from your first experience, how much force do you think will be required to pull the load up the slope? Record your prediction.

10. After recording your prediction, attach the spring balance to the load and try it.

11. Record the results. How close was your prediction?

12. Now predict the force required with the board on the second step. Try it after recording your prediction.

13. Was your prediction closer this time?

14. If your load weighed 100 lbs., how much force would you need to apply to push it up the inclined plane with the top of the inclined plane resting on the first step?

15. Think of some ways inclined planes would be useful. Write down two of them and show them to your teacher.

Teacher Information

An *inclined plane* is a slanting surface. It provides a mechanical advantage of force. We can move a load up an inclined plane with less force than would be indicated by the actual weight of the object (provided the friction isn't too great).

As with the use of any other machine, the total work required is not reduced but only redistributed. The advantage gained in force is sacrificed in distance and speed.

Mechanical advantage is computed by dividing the length of the inclined plane by the height, as in Figure 18.3-3.

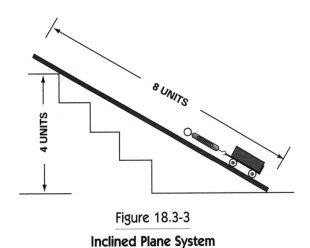

Figure 18.3-3

Inclined Plane System

The weight of the object is twice the force required to move the object up the ramp (if friction could be eliminated), but we must move the object twice as far as if we lifted it straight up (eight units instead of four units).

Application of the inclined plane is illustrated as barrels of oil are rolled up a ramp, as a car drives up a mountain on a winding road, and as a person walks up a stairway or up the sloping floor of a theater.

Note: If it is inconvenient for students to use a stairway for their work with the inclined plane, have them support the end of their board on a stack of books or some other sturdy, adjustable support.

INTEGRATING: Math, social studies

SKILLS: Observing, inferring, measuring, predicting, communicating, comparing and contrasting, formulating hypotheses, identifying and controlling variables, experimenting

Activity 18.4
WHAT IS A WEDGE?

Materials Needed

- Wedge
- Stack of books
- Board

Procedure

1. Stack the books up on one end of the board.
2. Place your fingers under the end of the board near the books and lift it up about 3 to 8 cm. Notice the force required to lift the books.
3. Now place the tip of the wedge under the same end of the board (Figure 18.4-1).

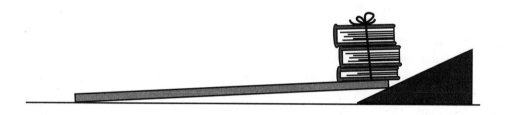

Figure 18.4-1

Board, Books, and Wedge

4. Tap the wedge with your foot, forcing it under the end of the board.
5. What is happening to the load of books?
6. Can you tell whether the force required to drive the wedge under the board is greater or less than the force required to lift the load directly?
7. Why does the wedge so strongly resist being forced under the board?

For Problem Solvers: Make a list of all the examples of wedges that you can find.

Teacher Information

Two wedges can be made by sawing a block of wood in half diagonally (Figure 18.4-2). Note that each wedge looks like an inclined plane. It differs from the inclined plane only in its application. When it is used as an inclined plane, an object (load) moves up the incline. When it is used as a wedge, the inclined plane moves into, or under, the object.

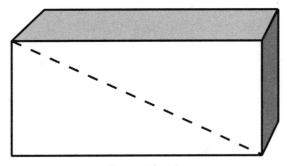

Figure 18.4-2

Rectangular Block of Wood Showing Diagonal Cut

We gain in force and also change the direction of the force by using the wedge.

The longer or thinner the wedge, the greater the gain in force and the greater the loss in distance; that is, the farther the wedge must go under an object to lift it a given amount.

The maximum distance a load can be moved by a wedge is the thickness of the big end of the wedge.

The ideal mechanical advantage of the wedge can be computed by dividing the length of the wedge by the thickness of the big end. However, because of the great amount of friction that is usually involved, the actual mechanical advantage is almost always significantly less than the ideal. Friction, however, is often helpful when using a wedge because it keeps the wedge from slipping out.

Applications of the wedge are the ax, chisel, pin, nail, knife blade, woodsplitter's wedge, and so forth.

Enrichment

If a short log, a sledge hammer, and a woodsplitting wedge could be acquired, a demonstration of the use of the wedge in actually splitting the log would provide an excellent experience in seeing the usefulness of the wedge. **CAUTION: Splitting wood may splinter, so use care and be sure children stand back a safe distance.**

INTEGRATING: Math, social studies

SKILLS: Observing, inferring, measuring, predicting, communicating, comparing and contrasting, formulating hypotheses, identifying and controlling variables, experimenting

Activity 18.5
WHAT IS A SCREW?

Materials Needed

- Pencil
- Sheet of white paper
- Scissors
- Black marker
- Large wood screw
- Ruler

Procedure

1. Cut a triangle from a sheet of white paper by cutting diagonally, from corner to corner (Figure 18.5-1).

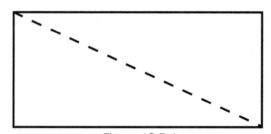

Figure 18.5-1

Rectangle Showing Diagonal Cut

2. Using the marker, make a heavy black line along the hypotenuse (the longest side), as in Figure 18.5-2.

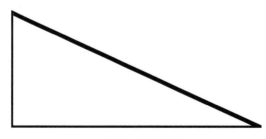

Figure 18.5-2

Triangle with Darkened Hypotenuse

352

3. Hold the triangle upright on top of your table or desk. Which of the simple machines we have already studied does the triangle now look like?

4. Beginning with the short side, wrap the paper triangle around a pencil (Figure 18.5-3).

5. Hold the wrapped pencil side by side with the large wood screw.

6. Does the heavy line of the triangle resemble the threads of the screw?

7. How would you say the threads of a screw compare to an inclined plane? Think about how the triangle with its black edge looked before you wrapped it around the pencil.

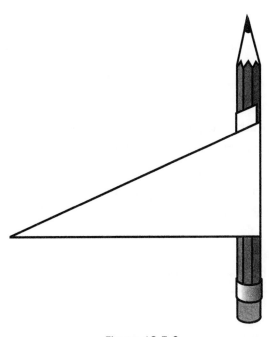

Figure 18.5-3

Triangle Being Wrapped Around Pencil

Teacher Information

The screw is a form of inclined plane that winds around in a spiral. The spiral-shaped ridge around the screw is called the *thread*.

INTEGRATING: Math, social studies

SKILLS: Observing, inferring, measuring, predicting, communicating, comparing and contrasting, formulating hypotheses, identifying and controlling variables, experimenting

Activity 18.6
WHAT KIND OF SIMPLE MACHINE IS THE SCREWDRIVER?

Materials Needed

- Wood screw
- Board (pine or other soft wood)
- Screwdriver

Procedure

1. Try to push the screw into the board with your fingers.
2. Place the tip of the screwdriver on the head of the screw and try to push the screw into the board without turning the screwdriver.
3. Did the screw go any farther than when you pushed with your hand?
4. Now turn the screwdriver as you press down hard with it on the head of the screw.
5. Can you get the screw into the board this time?
6. Notice how far the screwdriver handle travels as the screw turns around once.
7. How far does the screw move into the board as the screwdriver handle turns around?
8. What can you say about the gain or loss in force and in distance as you turn the screw into the board?
9. Make a list of ways people make use of the screw.
10. What kind of machine is the screwdriver?

Teacher Information

The screw offers a gain in force but at the expense of distance and speed. The handle of the screwdriver travels much faster and farther in a circular direction than the distance the screw moves into the board.

The screw also changes the direction of the effort from a turning motion to a pulling motion.

The ideal mechanical advantage of the screw is computed by dividing the circumference of the screwdriver handle (distance it travels in one complete turn) by the pitch (distance between two threads) of the screw. However, the actual mechanical advantage of the screw is greatly reduced by friction.

Friction helps by keeping the screw from turning backward or pulling out. The loss of force due to friction is made up by using another machine, the screwdriver. The screwdriver is a form of the wheel and axle.

The principle of the screw is applied in the use of the base of a light bulb, a bolt, a pipe wrench, caps on jars and bottles, and the piano stool.

INTEGRATING: Math, social studies

SKILLS: Observing, inferring, measuring, predicting, communicating, comparing and contrasting, formulating hypotheses, identifying and controlling variables, experimenting

Activity 18.7
WHAT KIND OF SIMPLE MACHINE IS THIS?

Materials Needed

Variety of simple and complex machines, as available, such as:

- Ball bat
- Bumper jack
- Egg beater
- Food grinder
- Pencil sharpener
- Rake
- Screw jack
- Tongs
- Fishing pole
- Broom
- Can opener (any kind available)
- Flour sifter
- Hand drill
- Pepper mill
- Scissors
- Shovel
- Tweezers
- Golf club

Procedure

1. Examine each of the devices. First, classify them into two groups—simple machines and complex machines.
2. Next, classify all of the simple machines according to the type of simple machines they are. Make a group of levers, wedges, etc. Then group the levers as first class, second class, and third class.
3. Now look at those you put in the group of complex machines. For each of these, make a list of the simple machines you see in them.

For Problem Solvers: Make a list of all the machines you have used today. For each one, name all the simple machines that are in it.

Examine a toy that has internal working parts. Think carefully about how it works and draw what you think is inside. What simple machines are there, according to your drawing? Do another one, and compare your ideas for each one with someone else who is doing the activity, or with your teacher or someone in your family.

Teacher Information

This activity will reveal what your students have really learned about simple machines. Try to allow them time to pursue the ideas suggested in "For Problem Solvers" as long as their interest lasts. Perhaps they can continue at home if necessary.

INTEGRATING: Math, social studies

SKILLS: Observing, inferring, measuring, predicting, communicating, comparing and contrasting, formulating hypotheses, identifying and controlling variables, experimenting

Topic 19:   Magnetism

TO THE TEACHER

A study of magnetism is often a very helpful beginning point for introducing structured inquiry/discovery activities. Be certain to warn the children that magnets can break or lose their magnetism if dropped or hit together. In the case of U-shaped magnets, a piece of soft iron called a keeper should be placed across the ends.

This material is nongraded. However, some activities may seem more appropriate to certain age levels. Each teacher should feel free to reorganize and eliminate materials according to the needs of students, keeping in mind the level of psychological development that may influence the understanding of certain concepts. Inquiry and the use of concrete materials is a major purpose of this unit.

The activities in this section seem to be most effective when presented to individuals, small groups, or teams. If your classroom organization permits, consider placing the materials in a science learning center, with time provided for children to move through the sequence at their own rate. Classroom discussions to reinforce the concepts should follow. If classroom demonstrations are used initially, children should perform the activities, and then the materials should be left on the science table for children to explore individually.

Many children are fascinated by magnets. They seem almost like magic. There is a natural desire on the part of many children to explore and share their discoveries with friends and others outside the classroom. Most magnets are fairly expensive, but many school supply outlets sell small magnets (for notices on bulletin boards, refrigerator doors, and so on) at a reasonable cost. If possible, try to get a number of these small magnets for out-of-school activities. Ideally, each child should have a pair of these small alnico (aluminum, nickel, cobalt) magnets.

One excellent source of magnets is audio speakers. Every speaker contains a magnet. They come in many different sizes and strengths and they are generally fairly easy to remove with a hammer and screwdriver. They are usually riveted in place; some are held with bolts and nuts. Check with a local shop that installs car stereos; they usually throw the old speakers away. Occasionally a speaker system in a school, or other large building, will be replaced and you might be able to get some dandies.

Bar magnets can be given new life by stroking them lengthwise several times across one pole of a powerful magnet. Stroke in one direction only. If poles are reversed, stroke in the opposite direction *or* use the other pole of the large magnet.

CAUTION: Audio tapes, video tapes, and computer disks are magnetic. If they come near a strong magnet, they may be erased. Spring-operated watch mechanisms may also become magnetized in a strong magnetic field.

Activity 19.1
WHERE DID THE FIRST METAL MAGNET COME FROM?

Materials Needed

- Nonmagnetized needle (with point broken off)
- Lodestone
- Paper clip

Procedure

1. Is the needle a magnet?
2. Test it by trying to pick up a paper clip or some other small object.
3. Rub it 20 times in the same direction with the magnetic rock.
4. Test your needle again. Is it a magnet?
5. What can you say about this?

For Problem Solvers: Check your reference books for the words magnet and magnetism. Try to find out who used magnets first, and what they used them for. What kind of magnets did they use? How did people make the first magnets that were made by people?

Teacher Information

Magnetism has been known for centuries. References to this "magical" property occur in Chinese and Greek mythology. This activity might provide opportunities for creative writing about the discovery of magnetism. Your encyclopedia can provide information about the history of lodestones.

The point of the needle can be easily broken off with a pair of pliers.

INTEGRATING: Reading, language arts, social studies

SKILLS: Observing, inferring, researching

Activity 19.2
THROUGH WHAT SUBSTANCES CAN MAGNETISM PASS?

Materials Needed

- Paper clip suspended from a string toward a large mounted magnet
- Variety of magnetic and nonmagnetic materials, such as a piece of plastic, wood, aluminum foil, paper, iron lid

Procedure

1. What keeps the paper clip up?
2. Place different materials between the paper clip and the magnet.
3. What happened?
4. What can you say about this?

For Problem Solvers: Find other materials to test. Can you find any material that is not magnetic and that will block the magnetic force and cause the paper clip to fall?

Teacher Information

Use a string to suspend a strong magnet from a mount or ruler (see illustration below). Place a paper clip held by a thread below the magnet, leaving a space between the magnet and the clip. The string can be attached to the floor with tape, or can be anchored by a book.

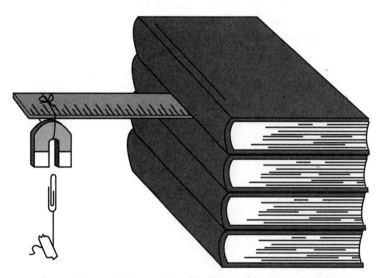

Large Magnet Mounted, with Paper Clip Suspended

Nonmagnetic materials will pass between the clip and magnet without disturbing the magnetic field. When the iron lid comes near the gap, the magnet will be attracted to it and the clip will probably fall. In a later class discussion, it should be demonstrated that magnetic materials will disturb or cut a magnetic field. However, substances made of a magnetic material (iron, nickel, steel, or cobalt) may be made into temporary magnets and behave like a magnet while in the magnetic field. Thus the iron lid alone may not pick up paper clips, but when it comes near or touches a strong magnet, it will temporarily become a magnet through a process called *induction*. The extent of time the magnetic material retains its magnetic properties is often related to its hardness (how tightly the molecules are packed together). The steel needle used in Activity 19.1 will retain its magnetism for a long period. A soft iron lid or paper clip will lose its magnetism rapidly when removed from the magnetic field.

There is no insulator to magnetism, but students will enjoy trying to find one.

SKILLS: Observing, inferring, classifying, predicting, communicating, researching

Topic 20:   Static Electricity

TO THE TEACHER

The topic of static electricity has at least two things in common with magnetism: (1) the attraction and repulsion of one object for another, and (2) the attraction of all age groups to the topic. There is something, perhaps the element of mystery, that intrigues both young and old. Although our information about static electricity is still based largely on theory (another common thread with magnetism), much is known about its behavior. Through observation and experimentation, logical explanations of the phenomenon have developed.

This section is suitable for virtually every grade level, and most activities can be easily adapted for use where needed. Activity 20.1 is intended as a teacher demonstration and works well as an introduction to the unit. If used this way it will raise questions, not provide answers, which is exactly what it is intended to do. A better time to discuss concepts is after students have experimented, discovered, and formed general ideas about the way electrically charged objects seem to behave. Static electricity works best on a cool, clear day (moisture in the air tends to drain off the charge), but success with these activities is very high almost any time except, perhaps, on a hot, muggy day.

Static electricity is the object of curiosity, annoyance, and humor. During a severe electrical storm the emotion associated with it can be fear, in recognition of the all-too-real danger to life and property. The lightning bolt itself is current electricity because it is moving, but it results from the buildup of an electrostatic charge.

Many of the activities in this section involve objects receiving an electrostatic charge by induction. When two materials rub together, such as wool cloth and a balloon, electrons are transferred from one material to the other—from cloth to balloon, for instance. However, a neutral object can receive an *induced* charge simply by being near a charged object. If a neutral object is approached by a negatively charged object, the neutral object becomes positively charged. If the neutral object is approached by a positively charged object, the neutral object becomes negatively charged. The induced charge is always opposite that of the charged object. Thus, charged objects are attracted to neutral objects. A charged balloon will cling to a wall, a person, and so forth.

As you select materials to use with static electricity activities, avoid those that have been treated with antistatic chemicals. Such chemicals are often used in dishwashers (anti-spot substances), in clothes dryers (anticling products or fabric softeners), or on carpets and furniture (fabric protector). Sometimes these treatments can be washed out, and the materials can then be used for static electricity activities.

Although wool cloth is often suggested for use in static electricity activities because it gives up electrons readily to other materials rubbed by it, cotton cloth, flannel, and many other fabrics work well. Be sure the fabric is clean and is *not treated* by a fabric softener.

Activity 20.1
WHAT IS THE KISSING BALLOON?

(Teacher demonstration)

Materials Needed

- Balloon
- Wool cloth
- String
- Permanent marker
- Words to the story (given below)

Procedure (for teacher)

1. Inflate the balloon.
2. Draw a face on the balloon, using the marker.
3. With the string, suspend the balloon from the ceiling. Adjust the height so the balloon is at the level of your head when you're standing on the floor. Do this while students are out of the room.
4. With students still out of the room, rub the "nose" of the balloon with the wool cloth. If properly charged, the balloon will now face you any time you are reasonably near. If you walk around the balloon, it will follow.
5. You are now ready for your students to return to the classroom. They should take their seats without going near the balloon.
6. Without revealing scientific principles involved, tell the following story as an introduction to your study of static electricity. Following the study, the Kissing Balloon could be used again for review and/or evaluation. A suggestion for such an evaluation follows the story.

Story

"Students, I'd like you to meet a friend of mine. His name is George. George, meet the smartest fourth grade in the state." *At this point you are standing at least 2 m (2 yds.) from George.*

"There are a couple of things I think you should know about George, class. First, he's nearsighted, and second, he has an awful crush on me. He likes me so much that he just can't keep his eyes off me—when he can see me, that is." (*Walk over closer to George and he will turn to face you.*)

"You see? He just stares at me, and he keeps staring at me as long as I'm close enough for him to see me." (*Walk away.*) "When I walk away, he just looks all over, trying to find me again." (*Move closer again.*) "You'll be able to tell when I'm within his range of vision because he'll look right at me." (*Walk around George.*) "See, I told you he likes me. Now, if you'll promise not to tell anyone, I'll let George kiss me—just once, on the cheek." (*Lean over, where your cheek is very near George.*) "Aw, that's so nice."

"Now, for the next few days, we're going to do a few things that should give you some clues about George. We'll visit with him again on another day."

The story can be adjusted to let it be one of the students that George (or Sue, or whatever you want to call ol' Bubblehead) is attracted to. Fun will be had by all, and your students should be more highly motivated for their study of static electricity as a result of meeting George.

Evaluation

One idea for an evaluation following learning activities on static electricity is to repeat the kissing balloon activity, put the following terms on the chalkboard, and ask students to explain why George behaved the way he did. Instruct them to use some of the terms from the chalkboard in their explanation:

- Static electricity
- Attraction
- Repulsion
- Transfer of electrons
- Induction

Note: One of the properties of static electricity is that a charge can be held in a given location. When you rub George's nose with the wool cloth, the charge does not spread throughout the balloon, but remains localized. Otherwise, this activity would not be possible.

INTEGRATING: Language arts

SKILLS: Observing, inferring, predicting, communicating, formulating hypotheses

Activity 20.2
HOW DOES RUBBING WITH WOOL AFFECT PLASTIC STRIPS?

Materials Needed

- Two plastic strips
- Wool cloth
- Sheet of paper

Procedure

1. Hold the two plastic strips at one end and let them hang down, face to face. What did they do?
2. Place the two plastic strips on the table and rub them with wool, stroking in only one direction.
3. Carefully remove the strips, touching them only at one end.
4. Place them together and let them hang down again, face to face.
5. What happened? Why do you think they reacted this way?

For Problem Solvers: The variables in this activity are what is being rubbed, how you are rubbing, and what you are rubbing with. Experiment with the variables. Does it have to be these particular strips of plastic? Does it have to be plastic? Do you have to rub with wool cloth? Might cotton cloth work? See what you can learn through your investigation, and share your information with the class.

Teacher Information

At step 1 the plastic strips are both neutral and therefore neither attract nor repel each other. When rubbed with wool, which gives up electrons readily, the plastic strips take on a negative electrostatic charge; they gain an excess of electrons. Since the plastic strips are now charged alike, they will repel each other when they are held up.

SKILLS: Observing, inferring, classifying, predicting, communicating, formulating hypotheses, identifying and controlling variables, experimenting

Activity 20.3
WHAT CHANGES THE WAY BALLOONS REACT TO EACH OTHER?

 Take home and do with family and friends.

Materials Needed

- Two balloons of the same size
- Two pieces of string 60 cm (2 ft.) long
- Wool cloth

Procedure

1. Inflate the two balloons and tie the ends with string.
2. Hold up the two balloons by their strings so they hang about an inch or two apart. How do they respond to each other?
3. Rub one balloon with the cloth and repeat step 2. What happened?
4. Rub the other balloon with the cloth and repeat step 2. What happened this time?
5. Explain. Discuss your ideas with your group.

Teacher Information

At step 2, the balloons are neutral and do not react to each other. At step 3, the rubbed balloon has a negative charge and it induces a positive charge in the other balloon. Thus, the balloons attract each other. When the two balloons touch, electrons are transferred from the negatively charged balloon, giving the other one a negative charge, and the balloons repel each other. When both balloons have been rubbed with wool, at step 4, they have like charges (negative) and will repel one another.

SKILLS: Observing, inferring, predicting, communicating, comparing and contrasting, formulating hypotheses, identifying and controlling variables, experimenting

Activity 20.4
WHAT WILL A COMB DO TO PUFFED RICE?

 Take home and do with family and friends.

Materials Needed

- Comb
- Wool cloth
- Puffed rice (several kernels)

Procedure

1. Rub the back of the comb vigorously with the wool cloth.
2. Bring the rubbed part of the comb near the puffed rice. Hold the comb steady and observe until you see something different happen. It might take as long as a minute or two. Be patient.
3. Explain what happened and why.

Teacher Information

The comb, being rubbed with wool, takes on a negative charge. When it is held near the puffed rice, the rice becomes charged positively by induction and will leap and cling to the comb. Patience is needed at this point.

As the puffed rice remains in contact with the comb, some of the negative charge (electrons) will drain off the comb and onto the puffed rice. The puffed rice now has a negative charge—the same as the comb—and will leap from the comb. Notice that the puffed rice does not simply fall, but rather appears to be thrown from the comb by some force. The force is the repelling action of like electrostatic charges for each other.

As the puffed rice sits on the table, its excess electrons will probably drain off to the table and the cycle is sometimes repeated.

SKILLS: Observing, inferring, predicting, communicating, formulating hypotheses, identifying and controlling variables, experimenting

Activity 20.5
HOW CAN YOU MAKE PAPER DANCE UNDER GLASS?

Materials Needed

- Sheet of glass (or inverted shallow, clear bowl)
- Plastic bag (clean)
- Two books
- Small bits of paper

Procedure

1. Support the glass by placing a book under each end.
2. Place some small bits of paper under the glass.
3. Rub the top of the glass vigorously with the plastic.
4. Observe for a minute or two.
5. What happened?
6. Why do you suppose it behaves this way?

Glass Supported by Books

Teacher Information

Avoid paper that has been treated in any way (for example, to make erasing easy). Tissue paper works well and plastic foam is an excellent substitute. This activity is very similar to Activity 20.4. (See "Teacher Information" in Activity 20.4.) In this activity, the behavior appears the same but the charges have been reversed. The glass will give up electrons readily and become positively charged. In turn, it will induce a negative charge in the bits of paper. The paper will jump up to the glass, gradually give up some electrons and fall back to the table where the process of induction is repeated.

SKILLS: Observing, inferring, predicting, communicating, formulating hypotheses, identifying and controlling variables, experimenting

Activity 20.6
WHAT DOES PUFFED RICE RUN AWAY FROM?

Materials Needed

- Clear plastic box (shallow)
- Puffed rice or vermiculite
- Wool cloth

Procedure

1. Put a few pieces of vermiculite or puffed rice inside the plastic box.
2. Rub the top of the box with wool.
3. What happened?
4. Bring your finger near the top of the box.
5. What happened?
6. Can you explain your findings? Do you think the puffed rice is afraid of you?

Teacher Information

This activity involves an induced electrostatic charge beyond that of earlier activities. When your finger approaches the negatively charged plastic box, your finger becomes positively charged by induction, just as the puffed rice inside the box has been. Therefore, your finger and the puffed rice have like charges. Evidence of the resultant repelling effect is seen as the puffed rice is "chased" around the box by the finger.

SKILLS: Observing, inferring, classifying, predicting, communicating, formulating hypotheses, identifying and controlling variables, experimenting

Activity 20.7
HOW CAN YOU MAKE SALT AND PEPPER DANCE TOGETHER?

 Take home and do with family and friends.

Materials Needed

- Balloon
- Wool cloth
- Salt and pepper

Procedure

1. Inflate the balloon and tie the end.
2. Sprinkle a small amount of salt and pepper on a sheet of paper or on your desk top.
3. Rub the balloon with the cloth.
4. Bring the balloon within about an inch or two (2–5 cm) of the salt and pepper.
5. Observe for a minute or two.
6. Explain what is happening and why.

Teacher Information

In this activity you will see the salt and pepper do a "dance" because of the principles explained in "Teacher Information" for Activity 20.4. You will need to caution your students to watch very carefully. Otherwise they will probably not notice that the same grains of salt and pepper are attracted to the balloon, repelled, then attracted again over and over. Notice that they don't just fall from the balloon but are *thrown* by the electrostatic force.

SKILLS: Observing, inferring, classifying, predicting, communicating, formulating hypotheses, identifying and controlling variables, experimenting

Activity 20.8
HOW CAN YOU MAKE A STRING DANCE?

 Take home and do with family and friends.

Materials Needed

- Balloon
- String 30–45 cm (1 to 1.5 ft.) long
- Wool cloth

Procedure

1. Inflate the balloon and tie the end.
2. Charge the balloon by rubbing it with the cloth.
3. Lay the string on the table
4. Bring the balloon near one end of the string, but don't let it touch.
5. What happened?
6. Can you explain why?
7. With practice you might learn to be a snake charmer!

Teacher Information

The end of the string in this activity is charged by induction and attracted to the balloon. Students enjoy making the end of the string dance.

SKILLS: Observing, inferring, predicting, communicating, formulating hypotheses, identifying and controlling variables, experimenting

Activity 20.9
HOW CAN YOU MAKE A SPARK WITH YOUR FINGER?

 Take home and do with family and friends.

Materials Needed

- Darkened room with carpeted floor

Procedure

1. Turn the lights off and make the room as dark as possible.

2. Shuffle your feet across the carpet for a few steps.

3. Touch a doorknob or some other metal object. Watch carefully at your fingertip as you touch the doorknob.

4. What did you see? If you didn't see anything, try it again.

For Problem Solvers: What is the spark? Do some research on lightning and find out how the spark from your finger might be related to lightning. Is lightning static electricity? Don't jump to conclusions—study it out.

Find out about lightning safety. What things are important to do during a lightning storm and what things should you avoid doing?

Teacher Information

This activity is not dangerous, but it does tend to invite horseplay, so if a group of students is involved, close supervision might be needed. The objective of the activity is to see the spark that jumps between the finger and the doorknob after an electrostatic charge is built up from shuffling the feet across the room on the carpet. Students usually discover that a spark can also jump between their finger and another person's ear or nose. The spark will sometimes be felt and heard. If the room can be darkened, the spark can also be seen. If some students are frightened by the spark, they should not be required to participate.

The spark might be thought of as a miniature lightning bolt. Lightning is a huge spark of electric current that results from a buildup of static electricity in the atmosphere. When moisture in the air and other conditions are just right, in balance with the electrostatic charge, the charge will drain off due to the natural tendency to create electrically neutral conditions.

SKILLS: Observing, inferring, predicting, communicating, formulating hypotheses, identifying and controlling variables, experimenting

BIBLIOGRAPHY

Selected Professional Texts

Carin, Arthur A., *Teaching Science Through Discovery* (7th ed.). New York: Macmillan Publishing Co., 1993.

Esler, William K., and Mary K. Esler, *Teaching Elementary Science* (6th ed.). Belmont, CA: Wadsworth Publishing Co., 1993.

Gega, Peter C., *Science in Elementary Education* (7th ed.). New York: Macmillan Publishing Co., 1994.

Tolman, Marvin N., and Garry R. Hardy, *Discovering Elementary Science: Method, Content, and Problem-Solving Activities*. Needham Heights, MA: Allyn & Bacon, 1995.

Victor, Edward, and Richard D. Kellough, *Science for the Elementary School* (7th ed.). New York: Macmillan Publishing Company, 1993.

Periodicals for Teachers and Children

Astronomy. Astro Media Corp., 625 E. St. Paul Ave., Milwaukee, WI 53202.

Audubon. National Audubon Society, 950 Third Ave., New York, NY 10022.

Cricket. Open Court Publishing Co., Box 100, LaSalle, IL 61301. Published monthly.

The Curious Naturalist. Massachusetts Audubon Society, South Lincoln, MA 01773. Nine issues per year.

Discover. Time Inc., 3435 Wilshire Blvd., Los Angeles, CA 90010.

Ladybug. Carus Publishing Co., 315 Fifth St., Peru, IL 61354. Published monthly.

National Geographic. National Geographic Society, 17th and M Sts. NW, Washington, DC 20036.

National Geographic School Bulletin. National Geographic Society, 17th and M Sts. NW, Washington, DC 20036. Published weekly during the regular school year.

National Geographic World. National Geographic Society, 17th and M Sts. NW, Washington, DC 20036.

Natural History. American Museum of Natural History, Central Park West at 79th St., New York, NY 10024.

Odyssey. AstroMedia, 625 E. St. Paul Ave., Milwaukee, WI 53202. Published monthly.

Ranger Rick. 1412 16th St. NW, Washington, DC 20036. Eight issues per year.

Science. American Association for the Advancement of Science, 1515 Massachusetts Ave. N.W., Washington, DC 20005.

Science and Children. National Science Teachers Association, 1840 Wilson Blvd., Arlington, VA 22201. Published monthly during the regular school year.

Science Digest. 3 Park Avenue, New York, NY 10016. Published monthly.

Science Scope. National Science Teachers Association, 1840 Wilson Blvd., Arlington, VA 22201. Published monthly during the regular school year.

Smithsonian. Smithsonian Associates, 900 Jefferson Dr., Washington, DC 20560.

Super Science. Scholastic, Inc., 730 Broadway, New York, NY 10003-9538.

3–2–1 Contact. Children's Television Workshop, P.O. Box 2933, Boulder, CO 80322. Published monthly during the regular school year.

SELECTED SOURCES OF FREE AND INEXPENSIVE MATERIALS FOR ELEMENTARY SCIENCE

Note: Requests for free materials should be made in writing and on school or district letterhead. Only one letter per class should be sent to a given organization. It is a courtesy, when requesting free materials, to provide postage and a return envelope. It is most important to send a thank-you letter when free materials have been received.

The following list includes only those organizations and agencies who specifically approved their being included in the list.

American Gas Association
Education Programs
1515 Wilson Blvd.
Arlington, VA 22209

American Museum of Natural History
Education Dept.
Central Park W. at 79th St.
New York, NY 10024-5192

American Petroleum Institute
Public Relations Dept.
1220 L St. NW
Washington, DC 20005

American Water Works Association
Strudent Programs Manager
6666 W. Quincy Ave.
Denver, CO 80235

Animal Welfare Institute
P.O. Box 3650
Washington, DC 20007

Freebies: The Magazine with Something
  for Nothing
1145 Eugenia Place
Carpinteria, CA 93013

National Aeronautics & Space
  Administration
Education Services Branch FEE
Washington, DC 20546

National Cotton Council of America
Communications Services
P.O. Box 12285
Memphis, TN 38182-0285

National Geographic Society
1145 17th St. NW
Washington, DC 20036

National Institute of Dental Research
P.O. Box 547-93
Washington, DC 20032

Procter & Gamble
Educational Services
P.O. Box 599
Cincinnati, OH 45201-0599

For more comprehensive listings of sources of free and inexpensive materials, see the following sources. Annual editions are available for purchase from: Educators Progress Service, 214 Center St., Randolph, WI 53956.

Educators Guide to Free Audio and Visual Materials

Educators Guide to Free Films

Educators Guide to Free Filmstrips and Slides

Educators Guide to Free Science Materials

SELECTED SCIENCE SUPPLY HOUSES

American Science & Surplus/Jerryco
601 Linden Place
Evanston, IL 60202

Arbor Scientific
P.O. Box 2750
Ann Arbor, MI 48106-2750

Astronomical Society of the Pacific
390 Ashton Ave.
San Francisco, CA 94112

Baxter Diagnostics, Inc.
Scientific Products Division
1430 Waukegan Rd.
McGaw Park, IL 60085-6787

Brock Optical
P.O. Box 940831
Maitland, FL 32794

Carolina Biological Supply Co.
2700 York Rd.
Burlington, NC 27215

Celestial Products, Inc.
P.O. Box 801
Middleburg, VA 22117

Central Scientific Co. (CENCO)
11222 Melrose Ave.
Franklin Park, IL 60131

Chem Shop
1151 S. Redwood Rd.
Salt Lake City, UT 84104

Creative Teaching Associates
P.O. Box 7766
Fresno, CA 93747

Cuisenaire Co. of America, Inc.
P.O. Box 5026
White Plains, NY 10602-5026

Dale Seymour Publications
P.O. Box 10888
Palo Alto, CA 94303-0879

Delta Education
P.O. Box 915
Hudson, NH 03051-0915

Denoyer-Geppert Science Co.
5225 Ravenswood Ave.
Chicago, IL 60640-2028

Didax Educational Resources
One Centennial Dr.
Peabody, MA 01960

Discovery Corner
Lawrence Hall of Science
University of California
Berkeley, CA 94720

Edmund Scientific
101 E. Gloucester Pike
Barrington, NJ 08007-1380

Educational Rocks & Minerals
P.O. Box 574
Florence, MA 01060

Energy Sciences
16728 Oakmont Ave.
Gaithersburg, MD 20877

Estes Industries
1295 H St.
Penrose, CO 81240

Fisher Scientific
4901 W. LeMoyne St.
Chicago, IL 60651

Flinn Scientific, Inc.
131 Flinn St.
P.O. Box 219
Batavia, IL 60510

Forestry Suppliers, Inc.
P.O. Box 8397
Jackson, MS 39284-8397

Frey Scientific
905 Hickory Lane
P.O. Box 8101
Mansfield, OH 44901-8101

General Supply Corp.
303 Commerce Park Dr.
P.O. Box 9347
Jackson, MS 39286-9347

Grau-Hall Scientific
6501 Elvas Ave.
Sacramento, CA 95819

Hawks, Owls & Wildlife
R.D. 1, Box 293
Buskirk, NY 12028

Hubbard Scientific
3101 Iris Ave., Suite 215
Boulder, CO 80301

Idea Factory, Inc.
10710 Dixon Dr.
Riverview, FL 33569

Ideal School Supply Co.
11000 S. Lavergne Ave.
Oak Lawn, IL 60453

Insights Visual Productions
P.O. Box 230644
Encinitas, CA 92023-0644

Let's Get Growing
1900-B Commercial Way
Santa Cruz, CA 95065

Nasco
901 Janesville Ave.
Fort Atkinson, WI 53538-0901

National Geographic Society
1145 17th St. NW
Washington, DC 20036

National Wildlife Federation
1400 Sixteenth St. NW
Washington, DC 20036-2266

Radio Shack
Tandy Corp.
Fort Worth, TX 76102

Sargent-Welch Scientific Co.
911 Commerce Ct.
Buffalo Grove, IL 60089

Science Kit
777 E. Park Dr.
Tonawanda, NY 14150

The Science Man
P.O. Box 56036
Harwood Hts., IL 60656

Scott Resources
P.O. Box 2121F
Ft. Collins, CO 80522

Southwest Mineral Supply
P.O. Box 323
Santa Fe, NM 87504

Summit Learning
P.O. Box 493F
Ft. Collins, CO 80522

Tap Plastics
6475 Sierra Lane
Dublin, CA 94568

Teachers' Laboratory, Inc.
P.O. Box 6480
Brattleboro, VT 05302-6480

Tops Learning Systems
10970 S. Mulino Rd.
Canby, OR 97013

Uptown Sales, Inc.
33 N. Main St.
Chambersburg, PA 17201

SELECTED SUPPLIERS OF VIDEO TAPES, VIDEODISCS, AND CD-ROM FOR ELEMENTARY SCIENCE

Beacon Films
1560 Sherman Ave., Suite 100
Evanston, IL 60201

Carolina Biological Supply Co.
2700 York Road
Burlington, NC 27215

Churchill Media
12210 Nebraska Ave.
Los Angeles, CA 90025-3600

Elementary Specialties
917 Hickory Lane
Mansfield, OH 44901-8105

Emerging Technology Consultants,
Inc.
P.O. Box 120444
St. Paul, MN 55112

Encyclopaedia Britannica Educational
Corp.
310 S. Michigan Ave.
Chicago, IL 60604

Everyday Weather Project
State University of New York College at
Brockport
Brockport, NY 14420

Hubbard Scientific, Inc.
1120 Halbleib Rd.
P.O. Box 760
Chippewa Falls, WI 54729

Insights Visual Productions, Inc.
P.O. Box 230644
Encinitas, CA 92023

Instructional Video
P.O. Box 21
Maumee, OH 43537

Kons Scientific Co., Inc.
P.O. Box 3
Germantown, WI 53022-0003

Miramar Productions
200 Second Ave., W.
Seattle, WA 98119-4204

Modern Talking Picture Service, Inc.
5000 Park St. N.
St. Petersburg, FL 33709

National Geographic Society
Educational Services
1145 17th St. NW
Washington, D.C. 20036-4688

Optical Data Corporation
30 Technology Drive
Warren, New Jersey 07059

Phoenix/BFA Films and Video, Inc.
2349 Chaffee Dr.
St. Louis, MO 63146

The Planetary Society, Education Div.
65 N. Catalina
Pasadena, CA 91106

Sargent-Welch Scientific Co.
911 Commerce Ct.
Buffalo Grove, IL 60089

Scholastic Software
730 Broadway
New York, NY 10003

Scott Resources
P.O. Box 2121F
Ft. Collins, CO 80522

Society for Visual Education
1345 Diversey Parkway
Chicago, IL 60614-1299

Tom Snyder Productions
80 Coolidge Hill Rd.
Watertown, MA 02172

Videodiscovery, Inc.
1700 Westlake Ave. N.
Suite 600
Seattle, WA 98109-3012

SELECTED SUPPLIERS OF COMPUTER SOFTWARE FOR ELEMENTARY SCIENCE

Apple Computer Co.
20525 Mariana Ave.
Cupertino, CA 95014

Carolina Biological Supply Co.
2700 York Rd.
Burlington, NC 27215

Denoyer-Geppert Science Co.
5225 Ravenswood Ave.
Chicago, IL 60640-2028

Emerging Technology Consultants,
   Inc.
P.O. Box 120444
St. Paul, MN 55112

Eureka!
Lawrence Hall of Science
University of California
Berkeley, CA 94720

MECC
6160 Summit Dr. North
Minneapolis, MN 55430-4003

Milliken Pub. Co.
P.O. Box 21579
St. Louis, MO 63132-0579

Optical Data Corp.
30 Technology Dr.
Warren, NJ 07059

Scholastic Software
730 Broadway
New York, NY 10003

Society for Visual Education
1345 Diversey Parkway
Chicago, IL 60614-1299

Special Times, Special Education Software
Cambridge Development Laboratory, Inc.
214 Third Ave.
Waltham, MA 02154

Wings for Learning/Sunburst
1600 Green Hills Rd.
P.O. Box 660002
Scotts Valley, CA 95067-9908

Videodiscovery, Inc.
1700 Westlake Ave. N., Suite 600
Seattle, WA 98109-3012